ECONOMICOLOGY:

The Eleventh Commandment

By Peter M. Wege

This page is printed on banana-fibre paper made from recycled paper with at least 3% banana fibres. The banana-fibre content is processed by students at Earth College in Costa Rica and is converted into paper by the Costa Rica Natural Paper™ without using harmful chemicals. A percentage of each sale funds scholarships for young Latin Americans who attend Earth College to learn the techniques of sustainable agriculture, knowledge these future leaders can take back to their own countries after graduation.

Economicology: The Eleventh Commandment

by Peter M. Wege

Illustrations by Mark Heckman

 First published in 1998.

ECONOMICOLOGY PRESS

A division of The Wege Foundation
P.O. Box 6388
Grand Rapids, Michigan

Library of Congress ISBN 0-9664367-0-9

Dedication

This book is dedicated to my personal hero, my Father, and my dear Mother. My father's inventive genius started the company that became Steelcase, and my Mother was his right-hand support and best friend. Together they taught me to love the God of creation and to respect His miraculous gift of life and this Earth that sustains us all. **Economicology: The Eleventh Commandment** honors my parents.

Peter M. Wege

Transport pilot Peter M. Wege had only one war in mind when he delivered an Army Air Force plane to West Point in 1943. He would serve his country until the Allies were victorious. Then he would go home to Grand Rapids, Michigan, and help expand the office-furniture company his father and two partners had started in 1912 as Metal Office Furniture Company.

But what happened in the black smog over Pittsburgh that day altered the course of the 23-year old pilot's life. Despite the clear blue skies around him, Lieutenant Wege could not see the city he was flying over. In a moment of epiphany, he knew that defeating fascism was only the first war he would have to help win to save humanity. A new and forever battle had to be launched to save the environment.

From that day to the publishing of this book 65 years later, Peter Wege has fought on every front to preserve this precious planet Earth. In 1969, he founded the Center for Environmental Study, an organization in Grand Rapids dedicated to raising public interest and knowledge about the environment. He served as Chairman of the National Pollution and Prevention Center at the University of Michigan. He chaired the Advisory Board for the Franciscan Life Process Center, a group of Franciscan sisters committed to living in harmony with the natural world and educating others about ecology and the Creator of this Blue Planet.

After serving in North Africa, Peter Wege *did* come home from the war in 1946 to help his father's company grow into the largest manufacturer of office furniture in the world, today's Steelcase, Inc. Working in Customer Service, Design Research & Development, Community Relations, and as a corporate officer, Wege contributed to the phenomenal success of Steelcase.

But his personal war to protect the environment never took a furlough. His time, energy, and financial resources have been directed at what he strongly believes threatens the survival of all life. This book is his labor of love, a collection of the best environmental wisdom he has read during the many years since his plane ride over Pittsburgh. If this book stirs the reader to think more deeply and act more caringly about the world we've been given, Peter Wege will know it has all been worth it.

Acknowledgements

I wish to acknowledge numerous persons who played a part in making this book possible, especially Sister Leonard and Sister Vincent de Paul who gave me a wonderful grade-school education at St. Stephens.

I'm indebted to Vicki, the mother of my family, who nurtured our children through *my* most formative years. For my beautiful grandchildren, I leave this book as their legacy. May they carry on this great cause.

To Ellen, Terri, and Mandy for keeping the Wege Foundation up and running so we can do good things like this book; to Susan, my editor, for finding the flow to my many years of quotes and notes; to Mark for brightening this environmental wake-up call with his witty and creative paintings.

ECONOMICOLOGY: THE ELEVENTH COMMANDMENT

Peter M. Wege coined "Economicology," in his new book, ECONOMICOLOGY: THE ELEVENTH COMMANDMENT. Economicology is the combination of economics and ecology; it is a fundamental basis for achieving sustainability. This work provides the reader with a breadth and a diversity of critical ideas and concepts drawn from the author's life experience as well as from important and valued writings of contemporary and historic individuals. This book, as a consequence of the insights and perspectives included, lays the foundation for Economicology. Accordingly, it is appropriate for the general reader seeking basic environmental information and the need to approach our use of resources in a more holistic, efficient, and systematic fashion. The sustainability specialist seeking perspectives on the concept of sustainability itself will also benefit from the issues addressed by Mr. Wege. The specialist will value the identification of the interactions that bind humanity together and necessitate the need for sustainability as the critical element for the world as we move into the 21st Century.

The author brings together his personal and practical experience in progressive environmental leadership and the insights of leaders in fields of Science, Philosophy, History, Government, Engineering, Industry, and the Social Sciences. The topics addressed extend from industrial ecology and solar power through population control and human consumption patterns. Peter M. Wege identifies the following six "E"s of our future: Economics, Environment, Ecology, Ethics, Empathy, and Education. According to the author, the survival of humanity depends on our recognizing that these six "E"s are inseparable. The educational activities and research efforts of the National Pollution Prevention Center for Higher Education at the University of Michigan certainly confirm the messages presented in this book. Peter M. Wege has provided a vital service to both the public at-large and the growing community of sustainability specialists through the preparation and publication of ECONOMICOLOGY: THE ELEVENTH COMMANDMENT.

Jonathan W. Bulkley
Professor of Natural Resources
Professor of Civil and Environmental Engineering
Director, National Pollution Prevention Center for Higher Education
University of Michigan

May 15, 1998

Extinct is forever.

Christian Science Monitor
on endangered species.

We'll never make the future what we want unless we analyze what has happened in the past.

P.M.W.

TABLE OF CONTENTS

I do not feel obliged to believe that that same God who has endowed us with sense, reason, and intellect has intended us to forego their use.

Galileo Galilei

Prologue

Let us together concede that many—if not most—of the profound concepts and philosophies have already been enumerated. Given that, for me to try and reinvent the wheel of wisdom would be both presumptuous and futile. Consequently, the book you are reading is a result of my search for the best of the great minds past and present who have concerned themselves with the survival of our planet, and, hence, humanity. The insights you will find here impressed me enough to remember, and even, in some cases, to quote from memory. My dream is that you, too, might feel the power of their varied observations.

It was what happened to me one afternoon during World War II that started my scribbling down quotes from the best and brightest minds past and present. I was a shavetail pilot delivering a training plane to West Point on that clear and sunny day half a century ago. But I couldn't see Pittsburgh at mid-afternoon even though I knew I had to be flying right over it. The reason? A thick, industrial pollution lay over the entire city. In those war-industry days, plants were going full blast, and there were few laws on the books to prevent pollution.

Pittsburgh's smog was my introduction to environmental pollution. My passion to do something about it has only intensified since that long-ago afternoon. In the beginning, my intention in collecting relevant quotations was not to publish, but simply to extend the boundaries of my own thinking. Yet as my file of notes grew fatter, it struck me that what I was doing should matter to others as well. Indeed, I was gathering nothing less than the most enlightened ideas from some of history's greatest teachers, scientists, and philosophers. The collective wisdom from the past was speaking directly to the desperate environmental and spiritual problems of the late 20th Century.

The great thinkers of the past do have something to say to us on the eve of the 21st Century. Holistic medicine, for example, has come into its own as if we'd just discovered it. We think we're pioneering with our health push for more exercise and less fat. Yet 350 years ago, Frances Quarles wrote that a sound body is the result of "fasting and walking." We seem to think Depak Chopra's concept of spirituality as a major component of good health is original. But in the 17th Century, Quarles wrote that good medicine required treating the whole person, not just the body: "...walking exercises the body; praying exercises the soul; fasting cleanses both."

How simple, yet profound. In this age of CAT scans and MRIs, we can now actually see what Quarles understood intuitively. Fasting "cleanses" the arteries, walking protects the heart, and praying relieves stress and nurtures the whole person.

If civilization is to survive, we must return to some of the great thinkers of the past like Quarles. We must understand the inter-dependency of the human race and the life-support system we call Earth. We must realize this globe is made up not of separate nations, but one single entity of living things. So many Doomsday books have come on the market the last few years that people are both scared and confused. In order to ease the unnecessary fears and to clear some of the confusion, I have assembled a few of the highest truths discovered by wise men and women past and present. If we do not learn from history, we are destined to repeat it. As Krisnamurti says, "The future is now."

Hope is a flame eternal. If I didn't have it, this book never would have happened. The key to our survival as a species is to start now by teaching our young what must be taught to save our world. We must relearn how to live together with spirituality, love, and compassion so that we can pass those values on to our children. We must restore the generosity of the human spirit.

But without the backing of strong, moral leaders in both the political and business worlds, we don't stand a chance. Somehow we must make peace prevail long enough to unite the most powerful world leaders with the most intelligent thinkers. Such an international think tank must then focus on solving the critical problems of this planet and the human race who call it home. The good news is that precisely the kind of cooperation we must have is starting to happen.

Without a lot of hype or fanfare, in 1992 just the kind of strong, moral leaders I'm talking about formed a union of global electrical utilities and named themselves the E7 group, short for the E7 Network of Expertise for the Global Environment. These major utilities span the globe from North America to Europe and on to Asia with the common goal of protecting the environment while they sell their electricity. In only five years, these world leaders in the electricity industry have already been active in 40 sustainability projects in 17 countries. At their annual meeting in June 1996, the heads of E7 approved a common strategy of reducing their utilities' emissions of greenhouse gases.

But the current E7 chairman of Ontario Hydro, Dr. Allan Kupcis, made it clear that to get the job done, everyone on the planet has to get involved. In his company's 1996 progress report on the environment, Dr. Kupcis put it this way:

Ontario Hydro is proud to be part of this global leadership for sustainability, but we know that the success of an international effort ultimately depends on the vision and commitment of local, regional, and national environmental programs.

By joining hands across oceans, nationalities, and religions, the E7 group has shown what can happen when we choose cooperation over warfare. Neither mankind nor our environment can tolerate another war, whether "limited" skirmishes or full-out campaigns. Just as the business leaders of E7 have done, people of all political stripes and of every religious faith must join minds for the common good of man and for the the earth that supports us.

The breeze of divine grace is blowing upon us all.
But one needs to set the sail to feel this breeze of grace.

Ramakrishna

Stewardship is what a man does after he says, "I believe."

W.H. Greever

Chapter 1

Rene Dubos: Prophet of Economicology

Rene Dubos, the renowned microbiologist, understood the oneness of all living things as well as man's responsibility to care for it. In fact, the subtitle for this book comes from these words by Dubos:

> *Man possesses the power to change the living earth which nurtures and shapes man and determines his fate. They are thereby complementary components of a system. Each shapes the other in a continuous act of creation. To strive for environmental quality could be considered the eleventh commandment.*

Indeed, were Moses to bring down the tablet in the late 20th Century, surely God would have added one more law. "Thou shalt not commit abuse against the environment, but rather honor it with respect for sustaining life as we know it."

We have reached an environmental fault line where we must either face up to what we're doing to our planet or plan to join the dinosaurs. Our hope is that a combined world intelligence will follow the example of the E7 members and take up the responsibilities of stewardship we have inherited as a global family. My theory for how we must proceed is summarized in a word I've coined called "Economicology."

My father was one of the founders of Steelcase, the world's largest manufacturer of office-furniture. As his only child, I am keenly aware that our economics-driven society bears great responsibility for the abuse of our ecology. But it doesn't have to be that way. To make the case that our economy and our ecology can actually benefit each other, I have collapsed those two concepts into the word "Economicology."

American entrepreneurship has created the richest and most powerful economy on the globe. But this historical success story was written on the assumption we would never run out of natural resources. Now we know better. Our nation's knee-jerk planning let the lumber barons level entire forests allowing untold acres of land to erode. Federal and state laws are finally attacking this obscene disregard for the ecology of our world.

The good news on trees that give us, among other things, life-sustaining oxygen is that the United States has 70% more hardwoods now than we did 35 years ago. By law, the lumber dealers may harvest only as many trees as they grow, and all forests must be re-planted or allowed to be naturally renewed.

This overdue policy is working. Every single day in the United States, the combined efforts of the forest industry, state forestry agencies, and federal tree programs put new trees in the ground. But we can't let our guard down for the battle is not over. Too many independent foresters continue to clear-cut precious acres of young trees with the inevitable result of eroding the soil and clogging any nearby waters.

It actually surprises most people when they find out that responsible harvesting of old-growth trees and replanting saplings does the environment a legitimate favor. The reason is that older trees remove very little carbon dioxide from the atmosphere compared to the young, fast-growing trees that are more efficient converters of carbon dioxide into oxygen. Since one cause of global warming is excessive carbon dioxide, replacing older trees with younger one also helps sustain a healthy temperature for our planet Earth.

And one further blessing of trees is what they can do that the other natural resources like coal and oil can not. Trees can grow themselves back when they are cut! Ironically, those who would spare our forests by making wood and paper substitutes out of petroleum, steel, and aluminum do not grasp the reality that those raw materials—unlike trees—are finite and non-renewable.

But we must do even more than replant the trees we cut if we are to have a future. And that is my push for merging economics and ecology into a global ethic for the next century that can be called, "Economicology."

A business person's perspective of sound economic policy can dovetail right into an environmentalist's view of sound environmental practice. But even as committed economicologists, the one thing we must legitimately fear is what Toynbee called man's natural tendency to neglect responsibility for preserving the common good. The rationalization for this negligence is that somehow all our environmental problems will be solved by quick-fix technology. This book is a wake-up call to say technology without "caring for creation" will destroy, rather than rescue, this planet as we know it.

That is why my selection of writers and quotations has been driven by the need for panoramic thinking. We need to learn from those futuristic thinkers who have told us we must broaden our vision from the customary now-only focus to a generational attention span. If we are to have a future, we must plan for the long, not the short, haul. If we don't, we are like the gentleman sipping his drink at the ornate bar of the Titanic. "Well, anyhow," he mused as the water rose outside the portholes, "the damn thing hasn't gone down yet."

This only is charity, to do all, all that we can.

John Donne

Labor to keep alive in your breast
that little spark of celestial fire
called Conscience.

George Washington

Chapter 2

Economicology In Action

If our global Titanic isn't to go down, our best chance lies in America. As a country founded on the idealism of democracy and experienced in the development of industry, we must surely be capable of both ethical and creative thinking. At Steelcase, where the creative thinkers I know best work, one of our "conscientious" enterprises is called Revest.

Started as a subsidiary in 1989, Revest actually REmanufactures used Steelcase furniture and sells it at prices far below the new Steelcase lines. Revest takes in used Steelcase furniture, replaces damaged parts, puts on new fabric, repaints scratched surfaces, installs new hardware, and sells at prices that can be below the new.

When Revest opened its doors, some of our people feared Steelcase was going to compete with itself by selling its own furniture second-hand. Instead Steelcase has simply expanded its customer base and added to its bottom line. And a direct consequence of this market-place success is the steel, foam, plastic, and fabric by the trainloads now ends up in handsome offices instead of in landfills. As Revest sales material puts it: The price is affordable, the product is recycled, and the quality is Steelcase. I call it simply, "Economicology."

But for business owners to activate Economicology in their own plants, they need to encourage all employees to let their individual creative juices flow. As part of the Steelcase's ongoing push to conserve through reusing, the people in our fabric plant looked at our whole line of office furniture and had a stroke of sheer genius. Instead of sending truckloads of fabric remnants to landfills, why not recycle those scraps? Steelcase uses some of the recycled fabric as a sound deadener in one of its products lines. Voila! Money saved in buying panel filling; money saved in waste hauling; the environment saved tons of landfill refuse. Economicology in action.

Now this ethical and creative idea has evolved into a whole new system at our fabric center. The fabric scraps Steelcase can't use get packed into returnable wire bins and sold to a recycle company who, in turn, sells them to auto plants for sound deadeners in car doors. The recycler also sells Steelcase's leftover leather pieces to businesses that make wallets and key chains.

In a clear-cut example of how Economicology works, Steelcase made enough money selling fabric scraps to pay for the new dock door needed to fit the recyclers' trucks. More important for our children's future, however, is that fact that recycling Steelcase's fabric saves several hundred tons of waste every year from being dumped in our landfills.

Such American ingenuity is part of our heritage and carries with it the obligation of leadership. We must encourage similar brainstorming among the people of more traditional, less democratic nations who might lack the imagination for seeing new ways to do things that befriend, rather than abuse, the environment.

I see great opportunity if even a tiny fraction of the considerable wealth and energy in America will take up the cause of our planet. One specific medium could be the vast network of charitable and non-profit foundations now scattered and uncoordinated. If these foundations could come together to form a quasi "world brain"—not unlike the E7 collaboration among electric utilities—I know a new form of economic humanness could emerge. Global morality and ethics could thrust "Caring for Creation" into the mainstream authenticating environmental concerns for the Earth.

A lot of people are writing now about the ecology and the environment. But too often they seem to be writing for each other rather than for the rest of us. This book attempts to fill that gap by reaching the most important readership of all: the good Americans who want to hear the truth about the world they live in. The Americans I'm looking for want to know how to leave the world better, not worse, for their children. This is the audience I seek. I want my readers to find out what hasn't been done environmentally, what can be done, and how we can work together to find long-range solutions for complex problems.

What we face is not just a pollution problem, but a people problem. We need to teach people, especially the young, how to use our resources. We need to redesign products and reduce the amount of packaging they come in if we are to slow down the flow of refuse and waste products around the world. Again, from the company I know best as a founder's son, Steelcase is daily proving that in packaging product, less is more. And, once again, one of our great ideas came from one of our employee team's thinking.

With five casters needed for every rolling office chair, Steelcase buys a lot of casters! After discarding mountains of the plastic bags and cardboard cartons the casters were delivered in, a Steelcase team came up with a way to ship new casters and spare the environment. Now all our casters arrive in reusable plastic trays. Labor costs in the unwrapping time are saved, and the trash mountain is no more.

Instead of continuing to package all our new furniture in disposable boxes because that's "the way we've always done it," Steelcase now ships almost one half of our furniture without cartons. Steelcase shipped over 3.5 million pieces of uncartoned furniture during the last year. In other words, Steelcase sent out 29,918 uncartoned truckloads of furniture in 1997 compared to 6, 776 cartoned truckloads. Consider the mountain of cardboard *NOT* used in those twelve months alone!

Steelcase's three best selling chairs, Rally®, Criterion®, and Sensor®, are all delivered in polyurethane foam "buns" that get sent back to the plant where they are reused to ship the next load of chairs. A pilot study of four Steelcase dealers found that the more product shipped uncartoned, the greater the labor savings in warehouse loading and disposal costs, and the less the damage.

The goal at Steelcase is to minimize packaging whenever possible, which is a significant boon to the environment considering the company ships more than 30,000 truckloads of product a year. Since, as with every other business, the customer is always right, if buyers want cartons—often because the furniture has to be temporarily warehoused or if product configurations need cartons to ship safely—we comply. But at the same time, Steelcase tries to retrain customers' thinking toward reusable pads instead of cardboard. And Steelcase's cartons are made of light, corrugated paper made from recycled elements.

Shipping desks under reusable blankets and shipping chairs in smaller, recycled cartons are two nitty-gritty examples of how our company is cutting down waste materials. I offer them not to boast, but to encourage brainstorming on other concrete ideas business people and private individuals might come up with to preserve and protect our planet.

Yet in addition to stimulating practical thinking on the environment, I also want to remind readers about the magnificent wonder of our Earth in its orbit around the sun. I mean to inspire those who use this book not only with the knowledge of what can be done, but also with the awe of realizing how we fit into our galaxy and how our galaxy fits into the Universe.

I shall pass through this world but once.
Any good, therefore, that I can do,
Or any kindness that I can show
To any human being,
Let me do it now.
Let me not defer, or neglect it,
For I shall not pass this way again.

This planet is a divine gift. I shall not hesitate to do whatever I can to keep it well for those who come after us. They shall inherit the Earth. Let us make sure it is the same magnificent orb God created for us.

A vision without a task is a dream;
A task without a vision is drudgery;
A vision with a task is the hope of the world.

Anonymous

HECK
MAN

You can't escape the responsibility of tomorrow by evading it today.

Abraham Lincoln

Chapter 3

Vladimir Vernadsky's "Biosphere" and The Six Es of Our Future

My mission in this book is to convince readers that what is said here really matters. I have adduced quotes from great minds to present my case for the good of the planet. But the first question is how to get your attention. The second is how to get you to respond to realities that could save the system which nurtures and sustains us all. My prayer is for the collective wisdom contained here to jump start all of our motors about what must—and can—be done.

This is the story of the Six Es of our future. It is about the inseparability of Economics, Environment, Ecology, Ethics, Empathy, and Education. All the brilliant writers you will meet here fit into the mosaic of this E to the sixth power.

One of these pioneer thinkers was a Russian whose life spanned the era from Nicholas II to Stalin to the fall of Communism. Born during our own Civil War in 1863, Vladimir Vernadsky was a geologist who explored the chemical processes in the Earth's crust. Vernadsky's original research led to the study of solar radiation.

But Vernadsky's best known contribution to the Six Es of our planet's survival is the word he coined for life's unity: "biosphere." The biosphere, Vernadsky asserted, defines the connectedness of our life-support system. And long before a diminishing "ozone layer" started making headlines in the 1980s, Vernadsky had already recognized the precariousness of our biosphere's protective environmental blanket. Vernadsky described it this way:

> *The absolute upper limit is the region, over 70 miles about the Earth's surface, traversed by ultraviolet radiation. This deadly radiation is prevented from descending to the Earth's surface by an absorbing layer of ozone which is created by the radiation itself out of atmospheric oxygen. It has been calculated that if all this gas were gathered into a layer of pure ozone, it would be only a quarter of an inch thick. We may thus regard the whole of organic life as protected from annihilation by a quarter inch layer of ozone!*

Vernadsky went on to thank the trees and vegetables of the world for providing this lifesaving layer by creating the oxygen which is a necessary component of ozone.

As every school child knows, this same beautiful gift of oxygen provided by the greenery of our planet allows people and animals to breathe. Obviously any pollution diminishing our vegetable kingdom directly threatens the survival of man and animal as well. Those businesses that harm the natural world seem to have forgotten the principles of photosynthesis they once learned in grade school. Polluting the soil is a form of suicide for it kills the vegetation that we and our animal friends depend on for life.

Vladimir Vernadsky would be pleased to know research out of the prestigious Massachusetts Institute of Technology now suggests that "brown" businesses allowed to pollute would be better off financially if they operated under more stringent environmental controls. This study is really good news in terms of Economicology! It shows that the very states in these United States who are paying attention to the reality of our "green" dependence are also the states with the most robust economies!

In 1992, MIT Professor Stephen Meyer published this landmark study on what effect the tougher environmental laws of the past two decades have had on the economy. Professor Meyer's research was a response to the often heard complaint from the financial community that the cost of complying with environmental regulations was ruining businesses and costing jobs. Called the "environmental-impact hypothesis," this anti-environmental mindset of the 1980s was being broadcast in corporate boardrooms as gospel, but without any evidence.

Professor Meyer decided research needed to be done to find out if, indeed, the more stringent environmental laws starting in the 1960s really had been detrimental to the business world. The MIT professor ranked all 50 states on the strength of their environmental laws. He then measured each state's economic performance in terms of gross product, employment, construction jobs, manufacturing labor, and overall labor productivity.

What Professor Meyer's seventy-pages of statistics and graphs revealed is that states at the high end of environmental rules did not experience any less economic growth and development than did the states with weaker environmental rules. But the really shocking—and unexpected conclusion—was that the states with stricter environmental laws actually had stronger economies than the states with more lax environmental regulations.

As Professor Meyer put it in his study:

...states with stronger environmental policies did not experience inferior rates of economic growth and development compared to states with weaker environmental regulations. In fact the converse was true: states with stronger environmental policies consistently out-performed the weaker environmental states on all the economic measures.

In other words, businesses in environmentally friendly states at worst had suffered zero economic loss since the advent of the environmental movement in the 1960s. But even more exciting for Economicology is that companies operating in the "greener" states appear to actually prosper more than do businesses in the "browner," environmentally unfriendly states. In other words, according to Dr. Meyer's findings, the green of money and the green of landscape increase in tandem in the states where good, reasonable environmental laws prevail.

One of those environmentally green states is Wisconsin where farmers in the Lake Mendota watershed recently demonstrated how good care of the environment translates into good care of the wallet. Instead of just applying the same amount of fertilizers and pesticides as always, the farmers decided to test the soil first. By measuring the fertilizer rates in the ground before applying the nutrients, the farmers found they needed 50% less phosphorus over some 30,000 acres than they'd used in the past. Not only did this testing spare excess chemicals from entering the watershed, it also spared the farmers a collective $200,000 in fertilizer costs.

Talk about Economicology!

Do all the good you can, in all the ways you can,
To all the people you can, just as long as you can.

P.M.W.

Minds are like parachutes—
they only function when open.

Lord Devon

Chapter 4

Vernadsky: Early Warnings on Rain Forests and Overpopulation

Vladimir Vernadsky's foresight about the planet's ticking environmental clock also included a prescient discussion of the rain forests. The Russian geologist was one of the first people to recognize what a pivotal role the globe's rain forests play in the delicate system he named the "biosphere."

Over 70 years ago, in 1926, Vernadsky warned the world that the systematic destruction of rain forests could end all life on Earth. The rain forest's contribution of oxygen to the protective layer of ozone alone could not be replaced if the rain forests were ever destroyed, Vernadsky wrote. More immediately, reducing the rain forests jeopardizes the lives of over a billion people who call it home.

The thick foliage and complex root systems of rain forests hold 95% of the annual rainfall providing a steady water supply for the people who live there. A lot of this water is returned to the atmosphere where it helps maintain steady rainfall patterns. Cutting trees in the rain forest reduces the humidity and thus reduces the life-sustaining rains that keep streams and rivers flowing even during the dry seasons.

Over a billion men, women, and children depend on water from tropical forests for drinking and crop irrigation. Without the sponge effect of the foliage and roots, the heavy rains would cause floods and landslides. Without the sponge effect of the foliage and roots, after the rainy season was over, the rivers would dry up. Vernadsky understood the crucial role the rain forests' thick vegetation plays in making water available year around and for protecting the soil from water erosion.

Indeed, Vernadsky was a prophet in alerting the world to the importance of preserving rain forests. The Russian scientist understood the powerful climatic effect of tropical rain forests could be felt thousands of miles away from the tropics. Vernadsky explained to his readers that by pumping huge amounts of water into the atmosphere, rain forests help cool

Population, when unchecked increases in a geometric ratio. Subsistence increases only in an arithmetical ratio.

Thomas Malthus,
An Essay on the Principle of Population

EARTH SHOE
HECK
MAN

Chapter 5

Industrial Ecology at Work in Denmark

While Vladimir Vernadsky's appeal for an "evolved" approach to population control has apparently fallen on too many deaf ears, his optimistic vision for man's intellectual possibilities is closer to happening. One promising point of light in Vernadsky's futuristic concept of man's moral and intellectual evolution is what is now labeled "industrial ecology." A term first used by Robert Frosch and Nicholas Gallopoulos in 1989, industrial ecology is increasingly popular as the most realistic way for corporations to change their ways because it makes economic sense.

In effect, industrial ecology asserts that wasteful and harmful industrial processes are also less economic. If companies and industries work together to dovetail their operations, the by-products of one manufacturer can actually become the raw materials of another. Thus waste becomes no longer waste but a marketable commodity.

If "industrial ecology" sounds like pie in the sky, consider what is happening right now in Kalundborg, Denmark. In a sort of evolved food chain, one power plant, an oil refinery, a drug company, a sheetrock plant, a concrete maker, a sulfuric acid producer, a heating authority, a fish farm, and a greenhouse started exchanging their "waste" products in the 1980s. The environmental chain reaction begins when the Asnaes Power Plant recycles its waste heat as steam to power both the Statoil refinery and the Novo Nordisk Pharmaceutical company.

Before Asnaes began recycling its "waste" heat, the power plant simply condensed its steam into water and dumped it into the closest fjord. But Asnaes' "waste" heat now also warms a greenhouse, a fish farm, and enough homes in the nearby town to let 3,500 families turn off their oil-burning heaters!

But there's more. The surplus gas coming from the Statoil refinery was "waste" before 1991 because of its high sulfur content. By installing equipment to remove the sulfur, the

Harr tells the story of industrial contamination of two water wells in a small Massachusetts town that sadly confirms Well's pessimism.

H.G. Wells' charge that we are about to extinguish ourselves is supported by the increasing evidence that certain cancers are linked to environmental pollution. In 1997, the National Cancer Institute announced that childhood cancers are increasing at the rate of one percent a year, making it now the most common form of fatal illness in children. Pediatric brain cancer, for instance, increased nearly 40 percent from 1973 to 1994.

With still no "smoking gun" proof about the cause of any cancer, these rapidly increasing numbers in otherwise healthy children point toward something in the environment. A New York times article headlined, "Cancer rates increase in U.S. children," quoted cancer experts as saying "toxins in the air, food, dust, soil, and drinking water are prime suspects" in the rising number of childhood cancers.

H.G. Wells knew that mankind is not guaranteed a future simply because we have a past.

> *We know that the everlasting hills are not everlasting, that all our working conceptions of behavior and destiny are provisional, and that human nature and everything about it is being carried along upon an irreversible process of change.*

According to Wells, man has two choices. He will act responsibly in his mission of stewardship for the planet, or he will tolerate irresponsible environmental acts like soil and water pollution. If man chooses to look the other way at industrial dumping, he can count on being pushed aside to make room for a surviving master species who *will* be good caretakers.

In order to survive as the life form created in God's image, mankind must rethink himself in a global, not tribal or national, context. As Wells put it:

> *It has become necessary for mankind to be re-educated as a conscious world citizen, to be prepared to take his place in a collective world fellowship, recognizing this as a framework upon which his social being must be rebuilt.*

My own childhood education as an environmentalist and as part of a larger world came in broken English from one of the Germans we'd gone to war against only a few years before! Barely a teenager during the war, Herman was put in charge of Russian Prisoners of War working a large grape arbor near Herman's village. Soon after the war, he came to this country bringing his knowledge and love of growing things with him.

Herman became my teacher in the early 1920s when my dad needed a gardener. Our family had moved from downtown Grand Rapids to the suburbs in 1920, the year I was born and eight years after Dad and two partners founded the Metal Office Furniture Company, now called Steelcase. Dad hired Herman to landscape our new home when the new immigrant was only 17. Herman spoke no English, but Dad spoke German so they hit it off.

As a little boy, I spent hours with Herman at his workbench in our garage asking questions about what he was doing to get ready for planting. He showed me how to put in asparagus, carrots, beets, lettuce, and green beans. I will always have fond memories of the pleasant young man who taught me as a young child to love the earth. From Herman I learned to respect the riches of the soil for the food it produces for all people.

H.G. Wells might have wished for more Hermans and fewer industrial dumpers in the lives of young Americans!

In 1939 when Wells wrote **The Fate of Man**, the Great Depression was barely over and World War II was about to begin. Private businesses were struggling to survive and bread lines were common all around the world. Little planning was happening in our cities that had grown up around rivers. At the time Wells published his book, those rivers functioned as the cities' sewer systems. But in those dark years between the Great Depression and the War, nobody had time to care. Just trying to find work left little energy for ecological considerations.

H.G. Wells knew, Depression or not, that people had to start taking an objective, long-term view of the world. Wells told his readers that this scientific view of the universe was far more important than politics. The English historian knew the global map would be redrawn after World War II, but it didn't matter to him. For Wells, realigning national borders was far less important than working on an expanded world vision for the future.

> *...and since the existing educational organizations of the world do not provide anything like that vision, nor establish the necessary conceptions of right conduct that arise from it, it (the world vision) needs to be rebuilt even more than the political framework needs to be rebuilt.*

Learning to think in terms of the whole world instead of separated nations would be a culture shock, Wells wrote, such as the world had never seen.

And so we find ourselves today living out Wells' prophetic warnings written over fifty years ago. We are still scrambling to find the answers to civilization's survival. Wells went as far as to propose a World Brain, a concept he wrote about in 1938. Had we embraced H.G. Wells' World Brain, embued with a global and ethical vision, we might have prevented the terrible deaths of World War II, Korea, Viet Nam, and the brutalities of the Soviet regime.

The world thanked Wells, even applauded him. But, just as Wells had suspected, the world went right back to sleep.

A politician thinks of the next election;
a statesman of the next generation.

Bernard Baruch

In all thy getting, get understanding.

Solomon

Chapter 7

Teilhard de Chardin On The Spiritual and Intellectual Unity of Man

Teilhard de Chardin is one of the most brilliant thinkers of the past century. His book **The Phenomenon of Man**, published in 1955, presented the limitless possibilities for man if we develop both our spiritual and our intellectual potential. For many readers, de Chardin's subject matter was too abstract.

But if we dig slowly into his provocative language, we can be sustained by a new level of comfort about the mind-body relationship. What the late 20th Century is rediscovering about the integration of each individual as a unity of mind, body, and spirit, de Chardin wrote about half a century ago "without the slightest doubt," as he put it.

de Chardin described this unity:

> *...there is something through which material and spiritual energy hold together and are complementary. ...there must be a single energy operating in the world. And the first idea that occurs to us is that the 'soul' must be, as it were, a focal point of transformation at which, from all points of nature, the forces of bodies converge, to be interiorized and sublimated in beauty and truth.*

A new respect in the medical world for this mind-body relationship is coming right out of the research labs. We now know that the body's front line of defense is the immune system. This means that an illness occurs when the immune system is compromised for some reason. And the fact that sickness often occurs after a period of emotional upheaval, stress, or depression used to get dismissed as a coincidence. No more. Neurologists have now demonstrated that nerve fibers originating in the brain physically extend into organs in the immune system.

Proving that brain fibers reach the immune system was only half the discovery. The other half is that researchers now know the immune cells themselves have specific receptors for receiving the molecules that travel along those nerve fibers from the brain. And to complete the communications loop from the brain to the immune system and back to the brain, research immunologist Ed Blalock has concrete evidence that chemical transmitters produced by the immune system end up in the brain.

These anatomical and biochemical links between the immune system and the brain confirm what de Chardin was saying. Our bodies are a unity. When we are mentally upset, our immune systems get the same "upset" message weakening its ability to fight off environmental germs and toxins.

In his book **Peace, Love, & Healing**, surgeon Dr. Bernie Siegel refers to this body-mind connection as the "path to self-healing." A surgeon trained to treat illness with a scalpel, Dr. Siegel's experience with his own patients has convinced him that mental attitude is directly related to physical health. Over the years, he's observed too many of his surgical patients with positive attitudes do better than those patients—often less seriously ill—who had negative attitudes.

Confirming Dr. Siegel's findings, a 1985 study in a British medical journal followed 57 women with breast cancer. The researcher found that five years after treatment, the state of the women's cancer was directly correlated to their attitudes about it. The researcher found that "recurrence-free survival was significantly more common among patients who reacted to cancer by denial or 'fighting spirit' than among patients who responded with stoic acceptance or feelings of helplessness or hopelessness."

After ten years, 70% of the patients with "fighting spirit" were still alive compared to 50% of the deniers, 25% of the stoic accepters, and 20% of the hopeless/helpless group.

These findings would not surprise de Chardin who understood this integration of spirit and matter. He believed that through each individual soul the natural forces meet and are reconstructed in the universals of beauty and truth. Thus man, the most evolved form of life, is the lighthouse for bringing together all living things in a union that values each life form as a necessary part of the whole. De Chardin wrote:

> *Man is not the center of the universe as once we thought in our simplicity, but something much more wonderful—the arrow pointing the way to the final unification of the world in terms of life. Man alone constitutes the last born, the freshest, the most complicated, the most subtle of all successive layers of life.*

Man's great potential is therefore also his great responsibility. As the "most complicated" living things, humans have a built-in obligation to nurture and unify the miraculous world they inherited.

This powerful theological thinker counted on the soul and consciousness of the human race to seek the absolutes of truth and beauty. By the gift of his superior abilities, man must follow the upward path as a necessary act of faith. "Have we the right to hesitate?" de Chardin asked rhetorically. Of course not, de Chardin asserted in **The Phenomenon of Man**. We cannot hesitate, and we should not want to. For de Chardin saw even better things ahead. For mankind, he wrote, the future holds in some shape or form "not only survival, but also super-life."

de Chardin's insights leave us with great hope. Like the other intellectuals quoted and discussed in these pages, Teilhard de Chardin believes in nature's progression forward in time. The process of evolution will continue to move civilization forward in syncopation with the forces of nature. Like the other writers here, de Chardin has forced us to think about what our responsibility to this planet Earth really is.

And de Chardin leaves us with reason for optimism in his conviction that man himself is evolving in an upward spiral. "We have said that life, by its very structure," de Chardin wrote, "having once been lifted to its stage of thought, cannot go on at all without requiring it to ascend even higher." In other words, the history of man in nature records no flat plateaus of development, but only continuous upward movements.

Teilhard de Chardin didn't think any higher order of being would ever supplant mankind. Consequently, man's ascension into a new unity will happen—not because it must, but because it will. "Man is irreplaceable," he wrote. "Therefore, however improbable it might seem, he must reach the goal, not necessarily...but infallibly." The issue of an ultimate unity in truth and beauty is not a matter of "if" for de Chardin, but only of "when."

Teilhard de Chardin's love of God is persuasive and evident in all he wrote. To him universal love is not only psychologically possible, but "it is the only complete and final way in which we are able to love." The time to express such love for all living things and the Earth itself is upon us.

Speak gently; it is better to rule by love than fear.

David Bates

No legacy is so rich as honesty.

William Shakespeare

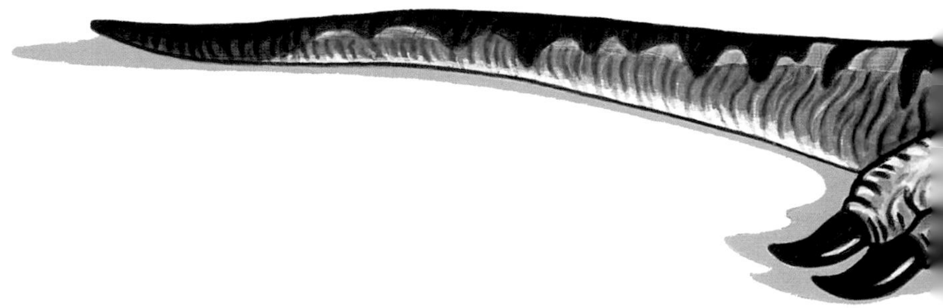

HECK
MAN

In wildness is the preservation
of the world.

Henry David Thoreau, **Walking**

HECK
MAN

I believe that man will not merely endure.
He will prevail. He is immortal,
not because he alone among creatures
has an inexhaustible voice,
but because he has a soul,
a spirit capable of compassion
and sacrifice and endurance.

William Faulkner

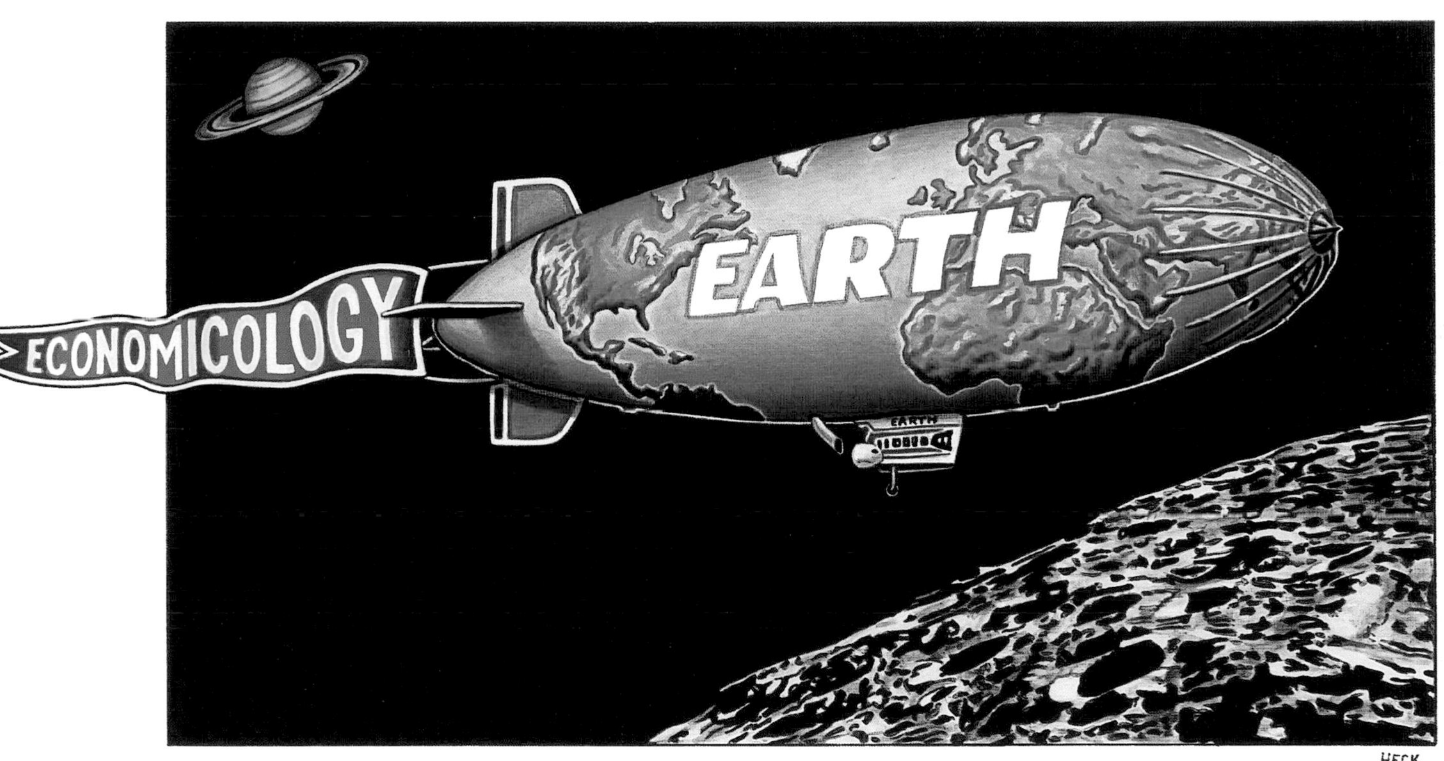
ECONOMICOLOGY
EARTH
EARTH
HECK
MAN

Chapter 12

David King's Spaceship Earth

Wendell Wilkie talked about "One World" when he ran for President in 1940. But in the half century since, that term has taken on a significant new meaning. In his provocative book, **International Education For Spaceship Earth**, David C. King described the concept of a global perspective as "a pragmatic thing...it means developing citizens who are capable of looking beyond the nation-state for the solution of certain problems."

We cannot continue to operate as though the problem existed "out there" some place having no affect on us as individuals. The frightening decreases in our natural resources, clean air, and water are forcing us to face the truth that we cannot continue to indulge ourselves in the luxury of complacency.

One of the first historical concepts we must re-think if we are to save this precious spaceship is that of sovereign nation states. The global patchwork of individual nations locked inside their restricted borders has been the history of the world; but it has also led to genocide and war. We can no longer afford to see ourselves as citizens of one nation, but human beings of one planet. Not until we reach this heightened level of understanding about our place on this planet can we solve the global problems we all face.

Evidence that we can, indeed, work across national boundaries effectively is becoming more apparent by the day in the world of international business. The first General Agreement on Tariffs and Trade (GATT) was established in 1947 with 23 members. The most recent round of GATT talks ended up with a document signed by over 120 countries. This latest GATT agreement cuts barriers to free trade and liberalizes international investment flows.

Significant regional agreements have similarly promoted interaction across borders among area trading partners. The North American Free Trade Agreement (NAFTA) and the Asian Free Trade Area (AFTA), and The Maastricht Treaty are the three important regional treaties that foster internationalism over nationalism.

*To waste, to destory our natural resources,
to skin and exhaust the land instead of using it
so as to increase its usefulness, will result in
undermining the days of our children the very
prosperity which we ought by right to
hand down to them amplified and developed.*

Theodore Rosevelt
Message to Congress
December 3, 1907

POLLUTION
HECK
MAN

Chapter 13

"Small Is Beautiful," E.F. Schumacher: Profit and the Public Good CAN Happen

In discussing the economic globalization of Spaceship Earth in the last chapter, we touched again on the optimistic potential that is this book's reason for being. Working together in borderless settings as the students from sixteen countries at EARTH College do, we can save our precious planet through Economicology.

Economicology is truly the synthesis of sound economics and preservationist practices. Our goal is to create a new mindset where all business decisions include respect for our natural resources. At the same time, we seek an environmental attitude that makes conservationist decisions with respect for the needs of the business community. In a world governed by the principles of Economicology, the tree-huggers and the three-piece suits are friends, not adversaries.

The ultimate benefactor will be, of course, the human race and every living creature on the planet. But businesses—both here and around the world—must broaden their perspectives. Operating on a for-profit-only basis won't do. What is exciting to report is that when private enterprises do operate within a framework of ethics and morality, those business owners discover their profits go up!

Good guys DO finish first. BankAmerica of San Francisco, for instance, negotiated an unusual loan to a lumber company. The lumber business could have the cash on one condition. It could not be repaid by clear-cutting forests. The same bank declined a lucrative deal with a big project in the Middle East. BankAmerica knew the borrower could pay back the loan, that wasn't the issue. The bank refused to lend the money because emissions from the proposed plant were excessive and thus environmentally damaging.

This same for-profit capitalist business has provided $6 million in a "debt-for-nature swap" with the World Wildlife Fund and Conservation International to help preserve one rain forest habitat in Latin America. Fifty years ago when BankAmerica first opened its doors, the founder, founder A.P. Giannini, established the bank's philosophy when he said, "Serving the needs of others is the only legitimate business today."

Giannini never heard the word Economicology, but he exemplified the principles which BankAmerica carries on today. Serving the needs of others does not diminish profits, but it's energized by a bigger picture than bottom lines only. For BankAmerica, based on its book value, this humanistic dimension to a capitalist enterprise works. Economicology contends that when the business leaders make decisions based on caring for family and community, their profits will still be there. But our world will be saved in the process.

In his thought-provoking book **Small is Beautiful**, E.F. Schumacher discussed the two dominant economic philosophies of the 20th Century: socialism and capitalism. Schumacher clarified both the strengths and weaknesses of capitalist economies compared to socialist. **Small Is Beautiful** was published in 1973 when the Soviet Union still ruled its massive empire on the economic principle of state ownership.

Beginning with the Bolshevik Revolution of 1918 when the state seized all private property, the USSR was a nationalized economy until the Iron Curtain fell in the late 1980s taking the Soviet Union down with it. Schumacher, writing before the USSR's demise, noted that private ownership in the free world had produced economic results far superior to those of the Soviet's nationalized economy.

> *The strength of the idea of private enterprise lies in its terrifying simplicity. It suggests that the totality of life can be reduced to one aspect—profits. The business man, as a private individual, may still be interested in other aspects of life—perhaps even in goodness, truth and beauty—but as a business man he concerns himself only with profits...*

The business man knows exactly what to do, according to Schumacher: "whatever produces profits." He similarly knows what to avoid: "whatever reduces them (profits) or makes a loss." By its very simplicity, however, this profit-only criterion ignores all other values.

Schumacher wrote:

> *Let none befog the issue by asking whether a particular action is conducive to the wealth and well-being of society, whether it leads to moral, aesthetic, or cultural enrichment. Simply find out whether it pays; simply investigate whether there is an alternative that pays better. If there is, choose the alternative.*

Now one successful entrepreneur has come up with a new value scale called EcoMetrics which evaluates business decisions in terms of both dollars and what he calls "God's currency." In 1973 Ray Anderson founded the carpet-tile company Interface, now a mega-billion dollar corporation selling carpet in 110 countries. Still president and CEO of Interface, Anderson has inspired his executive staff to take global leadership in environmentalism that includes making EcoMetric decisions.

In a 1995 speech to the U.S. Green Building Council and Exposition, Anderson explained EcoMetrics as a new way of evaluating production costs. Anderson used the hypothetical example of figuring out how much it would cost to produce one product that consumes ten pounds of nonrenewable petrochemically derived material. That number would then have to be compared to the cost of producing the same product, but reducing the nonrenewable resource to six pounds with the remaining four pounds coming from a benign, inorganic material mixed with chlorinated paraffin.

Anderson asked his audience of executives, "How do you judge the true cost or value of that chlorinated paraffin in God's currency?" In other words, how does one calculate the value of saving four pounds-per-product of a nonrenewable natural resource? Anderson described EcoMetrics as the search for God's currency by factoring into the costs of production the environmental impacts on everything from toxic waste to dioxin potential to aquifer depletion to CO2 emissions.

Clearly the simplistic nature of an economic system focused only on profits with no regard for human and environmental morality will, in the long term, destroy mankind and the Earth. Reducing decisions to the single question of how to maximize profits ignores the values that make us human and life worth living. What Schumacher referred to as "moral," "aesthetic," and "cultural enrichments" are the qualities that separate man from animals. They are the stuff of EcoMetrics. They are the tissues of life that remind us we are children of God.

As Schumacher noted, a major strength of capitalism has been its ability to drag the world out of primitive living conditions into a more comfortable state of material progress. Socialism's Bible, **The Communist Manifesto**, actually acknowledged the fact that man's for-profit motivations had improved life for the masses. Karl Marx's 'Manifesto' conceded it was the bourgeoisie who made the improvements in technology and communication that had drawn "all, even the most barbarian nations, into civilization."

Schumacher, like Marx, recognized private ownership has done a better job of improving living standards than state ownership of property has. One major reason is that government-run societies have built-in inefficiencies. Schumacher wrote:

> *It is not surprising, therefore, that many socialists in so-called advanced societies...are today wondering whether nationalization is really beside the point. It causes a lot of trouble—so why bother with it? The extinction of private ownership, by itself, does not produce magnificent results...If the purpose of nationalization is primarily to achieve faster economic growth, higher efficiency,and better planning...there is bound to be disappointment. The idea of conducting the entire economy on the basis of private greed has shown an extraordinary power to transform the world.*

If private enterprise has moved us out of huts into homes, what more does a socialist society have to offer? The answer is clear. Capitalism, by definition, relies on profit that does not take into account the public good. A socialist government, by definition, has the power to make decisions on a value scheme other than profit and loss—one that can include the public good.

In his 1993 book **The Ecology of Commerce**, Paul Hawken argued that there is a way to have the power of the Socialist state without sacrificing the freedom of a capitalist society. Hawken's thesis was that the institutions most aware of environmental problems—colleges and Sierra Clubs and Departments of Natural Resources—lack the power to make a difference.

Hawken asserted that the only institutions big enough to command environmental compliance are the businesses and the industries of the world. In other words, the same forces doing the most environmental damage are the only ones who have the power to preserve the planet.

Those of us who have been in a family business for years are proud of the fact we can pass this business down to the next generation. But this privilege also lays on us the responsibility for making sure the company we hand on is a good citizen. As Hawken said, big companies—like Steelcase—have the influence to make a difference to the environment.

We business executives must take to heart Schumacher's warning about what will happen if we see the world only through a profit-motive lens. We business owners must take to heart Paul Hawken's call for environmental advocacy from the power base we hold as employers.

We business leaders must emulate the A.P. Gianninis of BankAmerica and the Ray Andersons of Interface. We must make decisions that serve the needs of others.

Why take two
When one will do?

P.M.W.

If this generation had more respect
for Divine guidance,
It might have less need for
missile guidance.

Author Unknown

Chapter 14

Schumacher: Where to Put Nuclear Waste?

Unfortunately, the beyond-profit visions shared by Ray Anderson, A.P. Giannini, and the decision-makers at Steelcase are not the only attitudes among business leaders. While the broad-thinking CEOs are making an environmental difference by basing their business judgements on what Schumacher called "the meaning and purpose of life," many others have not caught up. In **Small Is Beautiful**, E.F. Schumacher was talking about the bottom-line-only business types when he wrote:

> *It is no accident that successful businessmen are often astonishingly primitive; they live in a world made primitive by this process of reduction. They fit into this simplified version of the world and are satisfied with it.... As a result, their judgments on actions dictated by a more comprehensive outlook on the meaning and purpose of life are generally quite worthless...*

The time is *now* for those business leaders to adopt a "more comprehensive outlook" that includes creative solutions to the very real dangers of annihilation. Schumacher cited the stockpiling of nuclear weapons as an example of a global problem calling for creative solutions.

World War II won the war against Facism. But Enrico Fermi's lab at the University of Chicago that shortened the war with the discovery of nuclear fission also launched the nuclear age. The atom bomb that forced Japan's surrender introduced us to a new kind of energy capable of destroying the world. If the nightmare nuclear war we dreaded between the USSR and the West faded with the fall of Communism in the 1980s, the potential for a nuclear catastrophe has not gone away. Now it is the stuff of movies.

The blockbuster movie *The Peacemaker* features terrorists getting control of nuclear weapons from the former Soviet Union. The fanatics use the threat of a nuclear holocaust to hold the free world hostage for their own extremist politics. The plot is not that farfetched.

Kazakhstan—part of the former Soviet Union, for instance, housed enough nuclear missiles in enough different silos to almost invite terrorists. The combination of the chaos created by the Soviet's departure and the provincial nature of the Kazakh people made their stockpile of nuclear arms particularly tempting to political extremists.

Across the Caspian Sea from Kazakhstan are Iran and Iraq, both nations known as breeding grounds for political terrorists. *The Peacemaker* might be fiction, but the scenario for terrorists holding the world hostage as nuclear targets could easily prove to be non-fiction. With the advent of portable chemical weapons like anthrax, the smallest of nations can take the great powers hostage with the threat of biological warfare.

But if producing poison gas is illegal, producing nuclear energy is not. And in his book published during the Nixon era, Schumacher was already worried about how to safely store nuclear wastes. Schumacher quoted President Nixon's science advisor as being extremely concerned about a long-term plan for warehousing nuclear residue. Both weapons manufacturing and nuclear utilities were accumulating nuclear waste without any permanent protocol for safe storage.

Twenty-five years later, the problem is much more serious as this country's stockpile of nuclear debris continues to grow. Yet, as the century ends, we still lack a fail-safe method for disposing of, neutralizing, or annihilating our nuclear trash. Not that there's been a shortage of ideas on what to do with our "hot" trash. Various scientists have suggested burying it under Antarctic ice, injecting it into the seabed, or hurling it into outer space. But the bottom line from most authorities—including the U.S. National Research Council of the National Academy of Sciences is that geological burial is, in the Council's words, the "best, safest long-term option."

Deep geological burial is the only workable solution because the radioactivity of the wastes from nuclear power plants—plutonium, strontium, cesium, and uranium isotopes—will neither decay nor go away for 10,000 years! We now know that one-millionth of one gram of plutonium can cause lung cancer. To build more nuclear reactors before we figure out where to put the radioactive residue we already have only increases the risk of deadly contamination.

The more we allow radioactive wastes to accumulate, the more we guarantee future generations a planet unfriendly to human life because of nuclear pollution. As E.F. Schumacher asked, "Why should we conduct business affairs as if people really did not matter at all?"

The current solution for our nuclear wastes are temporary cooling ponds next to every American reactor. Those ponds have been collecting radioactive wastes since the nuclear age exploded over Hiroshima in 1945. Half a century later, these cooling ponds are getting so loaded, they are at risk of getting hot. Exacerbating this danger is the fact that electric pumps are needed to circulate cooling water that prevents the fuel from overheating. A better temporary storage than these ponds would be dry casks that rely on passive cooling and could contain these nuclear materials for at least a century. By storing the waste in these dry casks for a hundred years, the radiation levels would gradually fall 90 percent or more.

The most seriously discussed permanent receptacles for our nuclear wastes are proposed underground tunnels built under Yucca Mountain—a barren, flat-topped ridge some 100 miles north of Las Vegas, Nevada. Since Yucca Mountain is in a former proving ground for nuclear weapons—the Nevada Test Site—the area is considered already contaminated. But the Yucca site is not without opposition. In late 1980, a group of scientists and engineers with the U.S. Geological Survey sent a formal letter of protest about the site to the Department of Energy.

These geological experts pointed out that Yucca Mountain in the Nevada desert is surrounded by faults—including the major Solitario Canyon Fault—and they noted that eight major earthquakes had taken place within 250 miles of Yucca since 1857. Finally, they argued predicting the weather over the next 10,000 years is not possible. If the rain should increase beyond the three-six inches a year now, the nuclear wastes could seep into the water table or the water table could rise to meet the wastes.

But despite these potential risks, most scientists strongly back Yucca and nobody has come up with a safer location. Understandably, just as everyone wants to see malls and dumps built in someone else's back yard, the people of Nevada want nuclear waste to get stored in somebody else's state. Clearly there is no perfect solution. But after $5 billion spent in studying Yucca Mountain, experts have concluded it is the best alternative so far.

Right now nuclear wastes are being stockpiled at dozens of nuclear power plants around the country. Putting all this dangerous material at one isolated site has to be safer than risking nuclear accidents at the many sites. Both the House and the Senate have voted to ship all this country's nuclear waste to Yucca Mountain in the Nevada desert by the year 2002, four years later than the federal government promised it would have a permanent storage site opened.

This proposed new law calls for first temporary and then permanent storage inside underground, concrete vaults. The waste would be transported to Yucca in specially constructed containers made of stainless steel or other metal. After being buried deep into the rock, these containers would be surrounded by an impermeable material such as clay to retard groundwater penetration. Finally, the containers would get sealed with cement or glass or both. Once the Yucca Mountain's first repository is filled, it will be sealed off from the surface with signs erected to the far-out future. These warning signs will clearly announce to generations thousands of years hence that deadly radioactivity has been entombed there.

President Clinton, however, has said he will veto this law already approved by both houses of Congress. So the stalemate continues. And the lack of any democratic solution on what to do with our nuclear wastes and our nuclear weapons illustrates E.F. Schumacher's argument about the inadequacies of both socialist and capitalist societies.

In the police state of the former Soviet Union, nuclear arms were under the jurisdiction of a ruthless system that killed and imprisoned without pause. Out of sheer fear, terrorists wouldn't have dreamed of trying to penetrate the Soviet's heavily secured nuclear sites. Similarly, the USSR could store its nuclear wastes in the safest possible spot no matter what the people said. But while this autocratic government could deter nuclear terrorism and safely store nuclear waste, it also denied all individual freedom.

In the democracy of the United States, on the other hand, elected leaders fear repercussions from their constituents if they make any unpopular decisions. And, for sure, any decision on what to do with nuclear waste will raise protests since all citizens want it buried in someone else's state! That's why this definitive legislation on shipping the nuclear waste to the Nevada desert has taken so long to pass. If we were not a democracy, the government would simply bury the waste under Yucca Mountain—probably in secret—and the citizens would not be allowed to protest.

Obviously, as Schumacher noted, the weaknesses in both kinds of government has led to bad results. The human dimension gets restricted to total state control in a nationalized government and hobbled by politics in a democracy. To solve the risky business of nuclear arms and nuclear waste, what we need is a government strong enough to act, but always with a human face. We need, most of all, according to Dr. Schumacher, to reconnect spiritually with a morality based on caring for our families, our communities, and all of Creation.

As business leaders, we need to concern ourselves with the broad spectrum of life and, since 1945, that includes the issue of nuclear power. While our day-to-day responsibilities require us to pay attention to our businesses, we must not limit our perspective to that alone. As Paul Hawken noted, by our power as owners and employers, we are in a position to influence other people. This lays on us a certain obligation to help make the right things happen to our world. Finding the best solution for controlling nuclear arms and disposing of nuclear wastes is one of the most right things we can get involved in.

We can no longer think in numbers only. We need to pay attention to goodness, truth, and beauty. We need to balance our entrepreneurship with our stewardship for the ecology of this planet. We have a responsibility far greater than our profit margins. We have a responsibility to the future of mankind.

Those who give too much attention to trifling things become generally incapable of great ones.

Henry A. Courtney

The biggest single factor in getting ahead is willingness to take responsibility.

W.G. Jordan

Chapter 15

R. Buckminster Fuller: An Operating Manual for Spaceship Earth

As we have seen, neither capitalism's for-profit system nor socialism's big-government approach can stop our abusive consumption of Earth's finite resources. But tapping the strengths of both individual creativity and governmental authority, solutions can happen. God would not have given us free will and the ability to think if He hadn't expected us to use those gifts.

In 1969, R. Buckminster Fuller wrote a book named for the only thing that did NOT come with this glorious planet: **Operating Manual for Spaceship Earth.** Fuller's thesis was that printed instructions were unnecessary because we have the gift of human intelligence. That means we can figure out how to take care of this green-and-blue orb without an "operating manual."

In order not to destroy ourselves by destroying the planet, we need to use the brains God gave us. To date, the Earth is the only place where humans can live. If we ruin it by using up too many resources, we could make homo sapiens not just an endangered species, but indeed an extinct one.

An engineer, inventor, and philosopher, R. Buckminster Fuller used his own creative intelligence to design buildings protective of the environment. The inventor of the geodesic dome, Fuller used the Spaceship image to remind mankind that we are not the center of the universe—even though we treat our globe as if we were. The truth is, no matter how huge the world seems to us, our Earth is only a speck in the total scheme of the Universe.

The earth is a mere eight-thousand miles in diameter. Our sun is 93 million miles away, and the closest star is a hundred-thousand times farther away from us than that! Obviously, if we destroy this planet through short-sightedness, our solar system will not miss a beat.

While Earth cruises through space at a whopping 64,000 MPH while spinning on its axis at the same time, the brilliant craftsmanship of our planet prevents us from feeling any motion at all. "Spaceship Earth," Fuller wrote, "was so extraordinarily well invented and designed that to our knowledge humans have been on board it for two million years not even knowing that they were on board a space ship."

As remarkable as the transportation design is, even more remarkable is the fact that Earth also has the ability to regenerate itself in spite of "entropy." The physical principle of entropy is the natural degradation of both matter and energy that ultimately leads to uniform inertness. Because of entropy, Fuller noted, the Earth must get the energy needed to sustain life from an outside source. In Earth's case, that source is the sun.

Fuller wrote:

> *Our sun is flying in company with us, within the vast reaches of this Galactic system, at just the right distance to give us enough radiation to keep us alive, yet not close enough to burn us up. And the whole scheme of Spaceship Earth and its live passengers is so superbly designed that the Van Allen Belts, which we didn't even know we had until yesterday (1959), filter the sun and other star radiation.*

The Van Allen Belts—also called the "magnetosphere"—are concentric layers of radiation around the earth named for the astronomer who discovered them. Like everything else about our brilliantly designed solar system, the Van Allen Belts work to preserve life on the only planet in our galaxy that can support plants, animals, and humans.

Yet ingeniously as Earth has been constructed, Fuller scolded his readers by pointing out how busy we have been "mis-using, abusing, and polluting" the operating system on which we depend for breath and life. We are so focused on our individual needs and wants, Fuller argued, that we forget the big picture of Earth itself.

Just as our own bodies must be understood holistically as flesh, mind, and spirit, so must this planet be seen holistically as an "integrally-designed machine," in Fuller's words. If it, and consequently we, are to survive, the Earth must be "comprehended and serviced in total."

Buckminster Fuller's grand strategy was based on what he called "our present navigational position in the universal scheme of evolution." In other words, the Earth has been able to support us despite our squandering its resources to this point in human evolution. Ultimately, however, our life-supporting necessities will either get destroyed or exhausted if we continue consuming them at the pace we have been. Fuller saw our only hope as being intellectually evolved enough to understand this reality and change our ways before we die out with our planet.

In an interesting analogy, Fuller compared what he called the "cushion-for-error" built into Earth's natural resources with a bird's egg. Until it is hatched, the embryonic bird is surrounded in its shell with all the nutrients it needs. Once hatched, the baby bird emerges into the world ready to fly. Like the hatching bird, man can no longer live in the mindless support system of an egg.

After millions of years evolving, man has now reached the stage where we must "spread our wings of intellect and fly or perish." Unlike the new bird, however, evolved humans don't have the luxury of leaving behind our "egg shell." We cannot survive without it.

The designer of the Climatron Botanical Gardens in St. Louis, Fuller called on both architects and planners to lead the way in "the largest scale comprehensive thinking of which we are capable." Fuller called on planners to share the leadership because they are trained to think with a broader focus than other people. In particular, Fuller pointed his finger at the politicians for taking a too narrow and too short-term view of environmental issues.

"How big can we think?" he asked rhetorically. His unspoken answer was that we can't think too big. And if we don't stretch our perspective in both space and time, one day none of us will be around to think at all.

Politicians, Fuller wrote, tend to obsess on how taxpayers will react at the next election. The result is that politicians are motivated to spend only the money needed for quick fixes, such as hiring more cops. But their reaction to the high costs of, for example, precipitating fumes to save our air supply is that we can't afford it. Fuller reminded political leaders that it takes "months to starve to death, weeks to thirst to death, but only minutes to suffocate."

If we are facing a shortage of good oxygen to breathe, our water supply is comparably at risk. Around the world, water shortages are a constant threat in the arid regions of Africa and the Middle East. Experts estimate that at least 80 countries where 40 percent of the world's population live experience droughts. That means four out of every ten people in the world already suffer the consequences of water shortages.

Egypt's 59 million residents depend almost entirely on the Nile River for water, and yet that water flows through eight other African nations before reaching Egypt. The Egyptians' serious vulnerability to a water shortage is geographically obvious.

Water shortages have started to show up in our own country, most often in California, as a result of both the growing population and water-intensive agriculture. The High Plains, or Ogallala, aquifer water system underlying 170,000 square miles from Texas to South Dakota is one of our major water resources. Yet the thousands of wells tapped into the aquifer for development and for agriculture have reduced the water reservoir by 11 percent in sixty short years. By 2020, a quarter of the Ogallala aquifer will be gone.

If we can't refill the Ogallala aquifer, we do have alternative water sources. Technology can desalinate sea water. The obstacle is, however, taking salt out of ocean water is expensive, and our political leaders aren't ready to bite that bullet. New York City, for instance, faces periodic water shortages which frighten everyone when they occur. Yet each time temporary water measures prevent the catastrophe, the old argument of "too costly to fix" arises again, and nothing is done. Fuller explained:

> *Our society adopts many such superficial palliatives. Because yesterday's negatives are moved out of sight..., many persons are willing to pretend to themselves that the problems have been solved. I feel that one of the reasons why we are struggling inadequately today is that we reckon our costs on too shortsighted a basis and are later overwhelmed with the unexpected costs brought about by our shortsightedness*

Buckminster Fuller was right. If a water crisis that can't be bandaided does happen in New York City, there'll be no time to build a desalinization plant for the city. The media pundits surely will begin writing headlines about "The Big Parched Apple."

In the same sardonic vein, Buckminster Fuller wrote that if we continue to see our world in narrow time frames, we might soon have to rename our planet "Poluto." The futuristic architect bemoaned the fact that even when sound environmental laws finally do get passed, our elected leaders say there's no money to implement those laws! Always, Fuller wrote, politicians come up with "more pressing, seemingly higher priority, new demands for the money."

Ironically, as Fuller, a graduate of the U.S. Naval Academy, pointed out, nations with no funds for saving our air and water still manage to come up with enough dollars whenever they need to wage a war. More and more often, Fuller argued, those wars get fought because the "have-nots" understandably want to share in the riches of the "have" nations.

But as with all the many and broad environmental issues Fuller addressed, the solution to the growing gap between rich and poor nations requires an evolved, longer-term perspective. If rich industrial countries better supported the poorer peoples of our shared Earth, the "have" nations would not need to spend precious dollars on wars. The money not invested in tanks and missiles could go toward such environmental saviors as facilities to take salt out of ocean water and to precipitate polluting fumes out of the air.

Buckminster Fuller was trained to always see the big picture. The Annapolis man had practical experience forecasting celestial navigation, pilotage, and logistics. He was also active in the long-range, anticipatory-design science that governed yesterday's naval theories and from which contemporary naval systems were derived.

In a happy example of international serendipity, during the same years Fuller was making his impact in naval and celestial affairs, Vladimir Vernadsky was coming up with the concept and word, "Biosphere."

Buckminster Fuller, the naval theoretician, warned us that our species was dead unless we began to retain more of the sun's energy. Spaceship Earth's remarkable ability to incorporate outside energy for its own life's purposes depends on our having enough of that external resource to keep going. Fuller saw the sun's radiation and the moon's gravity—supplying tides, winds, and rainfalls—as Earth's inheritance to be prudently spent and well invested for the future.

Fuller wrote:

> *...living only on our energy savings by burning up the fossil fuels which took billions of years to impound from the Sun or living on our capital by burning up our Earth's atmosphere is lethally ignorant and utterly irresponsible to our coming generations...Our children and their children are our future days. If we do not comprehend and realize our potential ability to support all life forever, we are cosmically bankrupt.*

We are also dead!

If we do manage to survive into the future centuries, it will be, Buckminster Fuller summarized, first, because we have not overpopulated ourselves out of existence. Second, we will have faced up to the simple fact we can't use up more air, water, heat, and energy than we've been given.

Third, we will have re-ordered our values enough to live with what we need and want because those needs and wants will have evolved both spiritually and intellectually. Finally, Fuller wrote, if we are still here, it will be because we have finally used our evolved scientific capabilities to serve the long-term needs of the entire world.

We will have discovered, according to Buckminster Fuller, that we are indeed too smart "to exhaust in a split second of astronomical history the orderly savings of billions of years' energy conservation aboard our spaceship Earth."

Fuller compared our fossil-energy resources to a car's battery. The energy stored in the battery is necessary to turn over the engine's starter, and then the battery's work is over. Once the car is going, the main engine runs on the gasoline pumped into the tank. If we are to survive, our precious and limited supply of fossil fuels must be treated like the car's battery.

Our finite treasury of fossil fuels must be reserved exclusively for building new machines that will support human life. But the daily intake of energy, like putting gas in a car, must come not from fossil fuels, but from the continuous energy sources of the Sun's radiation and the Moon's gravity in the energy form of tides and winds and rains.

Those continuous energy sources are more than adequate to run our major industrial engines. Indeed, Fuller noted, sixty seconds of a tropical hurricane equals the energy of a nuclear weapon. By saving our fossil fuels for the building of machinery needed to preserve our planet, "the celestially generated" forces of the universe can offer all the daily energy the planet needs to function.

Clearly, we cannot continue to use our fossil fuel and nuclear energy as we have. We must rely on what I call the "solar initiative." And we must put the environmental module of solar energy into every classroom from pre-school on up. But to launch this solar initiative, we must first accept the enormous problem of the Earth's increasingly burdened carrying capacity.

When Buckminster Fuller first used the word "synergy," not too many people had even heard the word before. But Fuller said it was the only word to explain how the behavior of the whole can't be predicted by the behavior of its parts. The solar system is synergistic because understanding each of its individual components still won't tell us how the system as a whole is going to behave.

I often open my talks on the environment by saying we started civilization in the Stone Age, graduated to the Bronze Age and Iron Age, and now we are in the Garb Age! As Fuller did with his geodesic dome, if we design environmentally sound products, we do not have the huge expenses of cleaning up. Even more important, such products will be toxic free, and we won't have to pay for the breakdown of health among the employees who made them and the consumers who buy them.

Solving problems before they happen is cost effective one hundred percent of the time. Economicology asserts that stopping any environmental pollution before it can happen will always be cheaper than cleaning up afterwards. Big business, big labor, big government, and big religions must lead the way in this preventive environmental maintenance. These powers-that-be must make themselves step back from their frenetic daily agendas to consider why we are here at all, and what our relationship to the planet really is.

We are running out of time. We are running out of time because we don't know how to bring the world's leaders together for the common cause of saving our life-support system. But the task is not hopeless, and we are making some headway. Unfortunately, it is still only the far-thinking few who understand the full gravity of the situation.

In this book, I am drawing on the best minds who have written on this subject in my overpowering wish to wake up my fellow citizens while there's still time. My dream is to spread the word far enough and wide enough so that everyone can hear the ticking of the time clock on our planet's survival.

All the technology and computer systems in the Universe will not be enough to save civilization unless we have the wisdom and intelligence to use it for the right purposes.

P.M.W.

THE GUZZLER

3 MPG City / 4 MPG Hwy

Chapter 16

Herman Daly: "What's needed is a change of heart."

Herman Daly's 1977 book **Steady State Economics** warned the world that our passion for unrestricted growth and our enslavement to the gods of technology would ultimately destroy the human race. Steady-state economics, according to Daly, requires a constant supply of physical wealth, or capital, matched by a constant stock of people.

But what we have instead thirty years later is an increasingly lop-sided economy. By producing more babies than we have deaths every year, the number of people dependent on that physical wealth has increased at the same time our excessive consumption has reduced the size of the "capital" pie.

We cannot run away from the statistical reality that the United States has the third highest population in the world, behind only China and India. Immigration—legal and illegal—gets the headlines for draining our nation's resources while rising birth rates get the back page. The census numbers quoted by Daly twenty years ago, however, told us even then our own country needed to control our rising birth rates just as the developing nations had to.

At the time Daly's book was published in the late '70s, the arrival of new immigrants had added only 30% to the USA's population growth. The real census boom, however—accounting for the other 70%—came from more Americans being born in this country than dying.

If we are to achieve anything close to Daly's steady-state economy, we must begin now. We do not need to march into the oblivion of the dinosaurs and passenger pigeons, but we will if we don't act with clear urgency. Specifically, Daly presented three major policy changes that must happen if we are to survive as a species. We must first reduce our use of non-replenishable resources by drastically cutting back our status-display consumption. In doing so, we will rediscover the simpler pleasures of the natural world now eclipsed by our addictive materialism.

If conservation and simplification were the first rules of change in Daly's formula for survival, the second requirement was to launch a "Scientific-Technological Renaissance." Such a "renaissance" would increase outlays for higher education and R&D; of even greater significance, the increased revenue for universities and for research would focus on solving environmental problems. The accelerated pace of research and education toward the good of the globe would include using solar energy, controlling pollution, conserving scarce resources, creating substitutes for our limited resources, improving contraceptive techniques, and enhancing agricultural productivity through ecologically sound methods.

The tragic reality is that a conserving, simplifying, and environmentally directed technology won't happen spontaneously. What will force these things to happen will be small disasters like gas shortages making it too inconvenient and too expensive to drive a car. These minor setbacks will be soon followed by major catastrophes including famines, epidemics, and genocidal warfare. These will be the terrible wake-up calls to all of us who share this planet.

Agreeing with other economists, Herman Daly said the Gross National Product is really the Gross National Cost. In other words, the popular economic indicator should be named for what it really measures—not the merchandise we manufacture, but the cost to make it. The more products we create, the more we drain our finite resources.

Indeed, the law of conservation of matter and energy should remind us that real output can not continuously increase without a matching increase in real input. As Julie Andrews sang it in *The Sound of Music*, "Nothing comes from nothing, nothing ever will..." If we go on building more and bigger products, we will go on using up more and bigger chunks of our natural resources.

Daly touched the hot button of GNP that must be addressed if we're ever to reach steady-state economy:

> *The question is whether further growth in GNP will in fact make us richer. It may well make us poorer. How do we know that it will not, since we not only do not bother to measure the costs, but we also actually count many real costs as benefits! These critics* (of Daly's steady-state theory) *simply assume that a rising per-capita GNP is making us better off, when that is the very question at issue!*

But if endlessly climbing GNPs are so destructive to our limited resources, why do the American people celebrate them? According to Daly, it's because, "Growth is a substitute for equality of income. So long as there is growth there is hope, and that makes large income differentials tolerable." In other words, we accept unrestrained growth because it perpetuates the American Dream. A rising GNP means each of us still has a chance to make our own fortunes. It helps make the huge inequalities of income and wealth palatable.

British historian and economist Arnold Toynbee said it this way a century ago:

> *More and more people are coming to realize that the growth of material wealth which the British industrial revolution set going and which the modern British-made ideology has presented as being mankind's proper paramount objective cannot in truth be the wave of the future. Nature is going to compel posterity to revert to a stable state on the material plane and to turn to the realm of the spirit for satisfying man's hunger for infinity.*

Way ahead of his time in seeing that we must find happiness within ourselves rather than in exploiting the material world, Toynbee was a prescient environmentalist and population-control advocate.

Like his 19th Century predecessor Toynbee, Herman Daly urged man to modify his consumerist ways by accepting natural limits to the size and dominion of the human kingdom. In Daly's terms, what is needed is "primarily a change of heart." But that change in heart must be quickly followed by a shift to an economy not requiring continuous growth.

The one simple reality we can all understand about endless rises in GNP is what they do to the finite store of fossil fuels that power most mass production. We WILL run out. Thus we have no alternative but solar energy which is both nondepletable and nonpolluting. Because solar energy has kept us warm for millions of years, the biosphere is adapted to it. Plutonium as an energy source, on the other hand, is the most toxic and dangerous substance known. Yet it is what fuels fast-breeder reactions upon which all our hopes for nuclear power depend!

Herman Daly outlined four inescapable truths about both our safe and our unsafe energy sources. First, solar power as a good energy alternative has not been pursued. Second, using plutonium is extremely dangerous and requires a kind of social discipline neither possible nor desirable. Third, we cannot continue to increase our electricity usage at 7% a year. Four, stabilizing our energy consumption at current levels would wreak no major hardship; Sweden and Germany use half as much energy as the USA does, and yet their living standards are comparable.

If we could manage to control our energy consumption, Daly wrote in 1977, and wisely use what we still have left in petroleum and coal, we'd have time to perfect solar-power technology. If the primitive people of Australia knew how to use the sun for survival, then our high-tech research labs in the late 20th Century should be able to do it too!

But if we continue to waste our limited fossil-fuel capital on trivial consumerism, we will never develop a solar-based economy. The real "energy crisis," said Daly, will not come from Middle-East sheiks and big oil companies, but from relying on fission energy to solve our problem of limited fossil fuels.

But with so much of the world economy dependent on fossil fuels, how do we overcome this financial need for the depletable, polluting, energy sources? Easy, according to Daly. Price the nonrenewables at the same level as the renewable sources. Instead of solar energy costing more than gas to heat our homes, gas needs to be pricier than sunlight. Daly wrote:

> *Once we accept the fact that the price system is the most efficient mechanism for rationing the right to scarce life-sustaining and life-enhancing resources, then perhaps rather than 'money profaning life,' we will find that 'life sanctifies money.'*

Virgin timber, for example, should cost not a penny less per board foot than replanted timber. Daly argued that petroleum must be priced the same as its equivalent in sugar or wood alcohol, "assuming they are the closest renewable alternatives." In other words, our planet's precious NONrenewable resources have to cost as much as its nearest REnewable substitutes if we are ever to preserve our Earth through a steady-state economy.

By raising the prices on nonrenewable energy sources, we gain the additional indirect benefit of limiting pollution and waste. The law of conservation of matter and energy states that if we can decrease throughput flow, we also decrease the stocks of residue built up by that flow. And since entropy is lower at the beginning (depletion) end of the pipeline and highest at the output end, it is physically easier to control depletion than it is to control pollution.

Complicated as this sounds, the simple fact is that less going in means a *lot* less coming out. Perhaps it is most obvious that monitoring and controlling the input is easier than monitoring and controlling the output when we consider how hard it is to measure the agricultural runoffs of insecticides and fertilizers into our rivers and lakes. Controlling the "depletion" as it were, end of the pumpline means not dumping all those chemicals on the crops in the first place.

Daly's steady-state theory asserted the best use of our natural resources would be to imitate Mother Nature herself in a closed-loop system of material cycles powered by the sun.

In this "natural" economy, durability, not disposability, is primary. Earth's resources could last as long as the sun continues to provide the energy that keeps the loop turning. Mother Nature's model, in other words doesn't say "bigger is better," but "durable is better," and includes my motto, "Do more with less!"

Like all the visionary thinkers quoted in this book, Daly sees the issue as ultimately a moral one. He wrote, "We have found it too easy to assume that future generations will be better off due to inevitable 'progress,' and therefore we are not to worry about the unrepresented claims of the future on exhaustible resources." By allowing nonreplaceable natural goods to get squandered and by allowing the population to grow unchecked, we punish the children to be born in the next century.

I think it is imperative now to take a long, hard look at what really matters to us in this world. That's when we'll realize this one big danger looming over us could deprive us of what really matters. For what really matters to us is peace, the end of crime and terrorism, a tranquil society, the right of privacy, and justice. Yet none of those universal dreams can happen if we overload the carrying capacity of this planet.

Forgive me for repeating myself, but it can't be said too often. Exacerbating all these environmental threats—from energy shortages to pollution—the single most frightening crisis we face is over-population. And this reality MUST be acknowledged by the world's political and religious leaders as well as everyone who has influence on that leadership.

Only when we make people aware can we change our patterns of producing too many people and consuming too many resources. Only then can the environmentalists, conservationists, family-planning groups, scientists, and peace activists merge their moral efforts in a global survivalist movement with enough political clout to get results. The alternative, as Herman Daly made clear, is nothing less than the end of life on earth as we know it now.

If we can learn to work in a political atmosphere free of intolerance and apathy, we can accomplish miracles. If we can incorporate Herman Daly's "change of heart" by ending our national love affair with more growth and higher GNPs, we can still preserve the human race. But to do so, we have to start with the basics. Caring for ourselves, our community, our country, and our Earth.

Chapter 18

Hazel Henderson: A New Work Ethic of Compassion

Economist Hazel Henderson's major work, **Creating Alternative Futures: The End of Economics** is a survival handbook for the future. Published in 1978, Hazel Henderson's thesis was as dramatic as her title announcing the death knell of economics. Henderson's book turned our traditional ideas about capitalism upside down. Indeed, Henderson's radical claim was that the free-enterprise world must redefine the sacred business concept of "efficiency" if we are to preserve our Earth and ourselves.

Instead of the business world's habitual "downsizing"—a euphemism for firing—to cut expenses, Henderson argued that businesses had to start upsizing by hiring more people. Her rationale was that the global explosion in population will require both the private and the public sectors to expand, not shrink, their work forces.

Contrary to every business school's curriculum on cost-containment, Henderson's position was that corporations must redesign their operations so that it takes more, not fewer people, to produce the same product. Henderson wrote:

> *In essence, we now have a surplus of human beings and a shortage of nonrenewable resources: thus we have to reverse our historical view of efficiency. It is only in a human-services society which is labor-intensive rather than capital-intensive that the resources of the earth will be conserved and human resources be expended for the benefit of human beings.*

In other words, our only hope for survival is to rewire our thinking so that our goal is to achieve *more* work and *less* product instead of the other way around. The economic law of less work for more product that has driven the economy since the Industrial Revolution can no longer sustain both people and our planet.

Hazel Henderson reminded us to keep our eyes on tomorrow's forest so that we don't get hung up on today's individual trees. She wrote:

> *Reality is what we pay attention to, and economists, like most of us, pay too much attention to short-term oscillations while overlooking larger cycles over longer time periods.*

Like a parent focusing on a child's short-term development rather than keeping their perspective on the child's growth over several years, economists agonize over quarterly dips in the economy instead of considering the next century.

Hazel Henderson summarized her topsy-turvy economics when she wrote, "We now have to realize, for most of the planet's inhabitants, what is needed is not labor-saving devices, but more ways of employing labor."

Over a century ago, the Victorian writer William Morris urged business owners to provide their laborers with work that "exercised the mind and soul as well as the body." Hazel Henderson's dictum to increase the number of people needed to do the same job could fulfill William Morris's idealistic aspiration for all employees. When it is economically feasible to do so, spreading the work load among more people could indeed make daily work less stressful and more fulfilling.

One common fallout from the ubiquitous corporate downsizing of the 1990s is that employees who held on to their jobs have had to pick up the work of their pink-slipped fellow workers who were not replaced. Because the retained workers felt lucky to keep their own jobs, they took on the extra work load without protest. But, inevitably, the increased time pressures put more stress in their daily lives making the work place that much less friendly to the human spirit. The stock market rallied to the layoffs that make giants like IBM leaner. But the "human-services society" Hazel Henderson envisioned as "labor intensive" at the same time took a nose dive.

Henderson recognized that diminishing the physical burden from workers faced with overwhelming demands of time-driven quotas would free their minds and spirits to do some creative thinking while on the job. Requiring less body stamina from each worker would allow that person to stretch mentally and spiritually while still getting his daily work done.

In the last chapter we saw that James Robertson, too, saw the future of employment as an opportunity for making the workplace a setting for human growth and creativity rather than a sweatshop for mindless drones. Like Henderson's book, Robertson's **The Sane Alternative** called on us to begin thinking of work as "self-actualization" rather than as self-demeaning.

Hazel Henderson argued that rising interest rates can no longer be the answer for allocating capital among society's "conflicting needs." What Henderson advocated in place of interest rates was that we restructure what we value. If we must learn to rethink what we mean by production-line "efficiency," we must also rethink what constitutes production-line "success." We must rewrite the time-honored litany of the industrial era that preached "standardization, competition, and hierarchy," Henderson wrote.

But an entirely new mindset crucial to our survival will demand a "new logic." Henderson saw this updated system of values as one in direct opposition to the earlier industrial mantra. Her revolutionary thinking called for a new economic principle "based on destandardization, heterogeneity, interaction, and a new ethics in harmony with nature."

But Henderson also recognized that such an extremist restructuring of our economic goals gets increasingly difficult as our organizations grow larger. The reason for this is the bigger the organization, the better equipped it is to manipulate employees by controlling and massaging information. Henderson quoted sociologist Bertram Gross:

> *...organizations are devices for screening out reality in order to focus attention on their own specific goals. Thus they regularly intercept, distort, impound, or amplify information, structuring it for their own needs and channeling employees' efforts toward their own goals.*

The American tobacco industry is a case in point.

Like the tobacco corporations, the bigger they get, the better they are able to select out the facts that enhance their own cause and the better they are equipped to screen out all negative responses. This manipulation of information in a pyramidal organization, however, can backfire on the executives at the apex. According to futurist Robert Theobald, the people at the top can get left out of the loop entirely.

Theobald wrote, "A person with great power gets no valid information at all." In other words, the result of exerting their best resources to control information coming in and out is that folks at the top can end up losing contact with what's really going on.

Fortunately, a form of business evolution has helped hold some of these overgrown organizations in check. Their very success keeps them expanding until, like dinosaurs, they get too huge to function effectively. According to Henderson, the positive result of this overgrowth is that when these behemothic entities die off, new forces of flexibility and adaptation are forced to come into play. The dinosaur dies, and out of its ashes rise diversity, experimentation, and continual learning that allows the whole system to change.

In her book, Henderson warned us that "the idea that obsolete organizations should be allowed to die" threatens a lot of people. The decline of a gargantuan organization, whether private or public, can cause "great social dislocations." And at the same time it is true that "less-productive organizations can wastefully divert resources" of energy, capital, and human creativity.

Thus, according to Henderson, the future will require us to act in one of two ways regarding our overgrown organizations. Either we let them die off when their manipulation of information prevents constructive change and creative thinking. Or we help them change themselves. Henderson believes our gargantuan organizations *can* be "revitalized by restructuring themselves and changing their goals."

To do this we must recognize the different roles of "insiders" and "outsiders" because they are vital to this process of adaptation. Theorist Warren Bennis calls the roles both insiders and outsiders can play as that of "change agents." Most of us are insiders, meaning we are directly involved with big organizations—both private and public. The primary organizations are where we earn our livings; the secondary ones are where we give our personal time, such as clubs, churches, and volunteer groups.

The outsiders are those who can provide professional and technical help, "whether from lawyers, architects, planners, doctors, or social scientists," Henderson wrote. Their expertise can function in advocacy planning to help "community groups articulate their aspirations and develop future plans." The more advocacy planners gain the respect and support from established institutions, the better equipped they will be to resolve conflicts between employees and the "dominant culture."

Hazel Henderson believed that these "outsider" advocacy planners could play an important role in improving the balance between the big organizations and the individual workers, between the majority culture and the minority. But she added that what was needed most of all was "a less wasteful economy geared more to filling the basic needs of poorer citizens than encouraging the over-consumption of the middle and affluent classes." Instead of concocting new luxuries for the middle and upper classes, Henderson advised us to focus on the elemental needs of the lower class. If we do not move in this direction soon, Henderson argued, we face certain global conflicts—both small and large.

Hazel Henderson was not the only prophet-scholar to warn us about the growing gap between the haves of the world and the have-nots. In his book **An Inquiry into the Human**

Prospect, Robert Heilbroner similarly suggested that ignoring the needs of the underclass will inevitably lead to increasing sabotage and terrorism against the rich countries by Third World guerrillas. Barry Commoner, in his book **The Closing Circle**, also wrote at length about the immoral plight of rich countries that use most of the world's resources and, thus, create most of the pollution. In this country alone, we consume 36% of the world's natural resources even though we're only 6% of the world's population.

Hazel Henderson pointed out that even America's love affair with beef takes bread from the mouths of the world's poor because raising livestock requires huge quantities of grains. She wrote, "A reduction of meat consumption would release grain wastefully used to fatten livestock for direct human consumption by the world's needy." From our tables to our closets to our garages, we must dial down our consumption of the world's finite resources. And based on my mail box, we need to act soon. Every day I am flooded with catalogs selling ever-more frivolous products.

As the active manufacturing of goods continues to move overseas where labor is cheaper, we need to be as environmentally vigilant as we are at home. Underdeveloped countries far from the USA have their own natural resources and less polluted environments. We must oversee this transfer of production so that those distant resources do not get squandered nor those healthy environments destroyed. "We are the World," as the song goes. We have a moral responsibility to monitor overseas production if we are to secure an environmentally rich future for the generations not yet born.

One of the most startling, and yet encouraging, observations in Hazel Henderson's book is that her research indicated as many as 90% of all Americans think the government does not tell them the hard truths. Of particular interest, this significant majority of Americans think the government is not honest about energy.

The positive spin from Henderson's finding is that Americans already suspect the truth about the depletion of the world's natural resources, and they want to act morally to preserve the environment. Three to one, according to Henderson, Americans agree that most of our leaders don't understand their constituents "want quality of almost everything" over quantity. In other words, the majority of us have been saying for some time that we'd prefer to live with *better* things, not *more* things.

Hazel Henderson's book noted that we Americans, by and large, think it is morally wrong for this nation to consume a lopsided share of the world's natural resources; and we're willing to alter our life styles to stop doing it. According to Henderson, eating less meat, not buying the newest car model every year, and reducing advertising would be three good starts.

And start we must. The CO_2 in our atmosphere is rising annually as the population grows exponentially. Every fifty years, the human population is doubling. If this continues, it's only a matter of time until the have-nots actually take up arms against the haves. If we do not achieve a balance between economics and ecology, we can expect full-scale anarchy one day. If we disregard the life-support system we live on, it will fail us in the not-so-distant future.

If the CO_2 level threatens our planet, so, too, do the electric utilities by aggressively substituting nuclear power for less costly and less violent technologies. To achieve their so-called efficiencies, these nuclear-fueled electric companies are imposing on Americans risks we didn't choose. The deadly plutonium, for instance, necessary to nuclear power will require elaborate police and security systems for thousands of years to come.

And this choice is being made despite the fact that clean and safe solar heating can provide an equivalent energy supply while simultaneously creating several times more jobs per dollar than providing nuclear energy can. In accordance with Hazel Henderson's call for a more labor-intensive economy, safe, solar energy can provide meaningful employment for more people as well as saving us from the disastrous possibilities of nuclear-power plants.

With more jobs per dollar a worthy investment goal, solar energy defeats nuclear energy hands down. In fact, conservation itself can and should become our major new energy source. When we don't spend our natural resources, we conserve them as a source. As Ben Franklin put it, "A penny saved is a penny earned."

One of Hazel Henderson's strong recommendations was for a full-scale international data bank on corporate accountability. The accountability data bank on what each corporation is doing in terms of its work force and its environmental habits is an idea that reaches beyond corporate competition. If we are to save the world from foolish men who make a mockery of the human spirit and human survival, we must embrace the kind of corporate responsibility Henderson advocated.

I urge all fellow executives of multi-national companies to come together for the greater common good. Only through love and compassion and respect for our fellow man and our employees—as well as through the understanding that our Spaceship Earth is reaching capacity—can we hope to survive. We must begin the process of creating a quality life that can sustain all of Earth's inhabitants decently and equitably. My philosophy of Economicology sees the way to achieving this goal is through more education and heightened awareness.

There is a destiny that makes us brothers,
none goes his way alone.
All that we send into the lives of others
comes back into our own.

Edwin Markham

All men are by nature equal, made, all, of the same earth by the same Creator and however we deceive ourselves, as dear to God is the poor peasant as the mighty prince.

Plato

TRUTH
HECK
MAN

Chapter 19

Heinz R. Pagels: The Cosmic Consciousness of God

In his 1985 book **Perfect Symmetry**, subtitled "The Search for the Beginning of Time," Heinz R. Pagels echoed Hazel Henderson's theme of human liberation. While Henderson focused on liberating people from excessive work and oversized organizations, Pagels called us to free ourselves from the restriction of our limited desires and affections. We are part of the Universe, Pagels wrote. And it is man's "optical delusion" that we are not part of the whole—that our thoughts and feelings are somehow separated from the rest.

Pagels wrote that our task must be "widening the whole circle of compassion to embrace all living creatures and the whole nature of its beauty." While such an ideal can never be fully achieved, just the act of striving toward it is not only a step toward the liberation, but it is also "a foundation for inner security," according to Pagels.

Idealistic as it might be, Pagels' dream took a giant leap forward in early 1997 when an Arizona professor won a hefty $10,000 grant from the prestigious John Templeton Foundation to teach a course embodying Pagels' very theory of unity. Professor of humanities and social sciences at Emory-Riddle Aeronautical University in Prescott, Tom Pagliasotti won the grant to develop a new course merging physics and theology.

Pagliasotti's class will help students explore the relationship between modern physics and a specific expression of modern religion called "process theology." Professor Pagliasotti described process theology to a news reporter as, "An ongoing sense of intimate relations, the relationship between the natural world and the way it affects us and we affect it..."

The course titled "The Prominence of Process in Modern Science and Religion" deals with subatomic particle physics in conjunction with God and Creation. Pagliasotti's class covers the 20th Century discovery of quantum physics that has shattered the pure objectivity of Newtonian physics. This century's revolutionary discovery in physics proved that the very act of observing something in fact changes the thing being observed. As Professor Pagliasotti put it, "One of the breakthrough concepts of modern physics is that somehow we are interconnected."

Professor Darrell Smith, chairman of the Arizona university's math and physical-science department, will co-teach the class with Pagliasotti. Professor Smith described the course to be taught for the first time in 1998 as "dealing with physics and religion and science and looking at where they may overlap." Particle physics has demonstrated there are tiny pieces of matter that behave in unpredictable ways. For example, a single particle may be in a million places at once. This radical new idea—called the "uncertainty principle"—asserts that there is no separation between the observer and the observed.

Thirteen years before this physics-theology class was put together, Heinz Pagels' book called for the liberation of the "attitude of Homo spiritualist." Pagels recognized the need for man to share in the cosmic consciousness of God. Pagels' interpretation of God as encompassing all creation resonates not only with 20th Century physics but also with the pre-Christian philosopher Plato and his concept of the Ideal. Pagels also harked back to the French philosopher discussed earlier in these pages, Pierre Teilhard de Chardin.

Teilhard de Chardin believed humankind was in the process of a liberating transformation toward such a universal consciousness as Plato described. Pagels' theory of "homo spiritualist" supported de Chardin's mystical vision of the future when the universal unity of matter and spirit and life would be fully recognized.

Like the English poet William Wordsworth who wrote "The child is father of the man," Heinz Pagels believed it is the child in us that is the source of our creative powers. He found the most creative people were those not held back by social and conceptual stereotypes. Instead of being bound by cultural expectations, creative people explore reality for themselves. "They are radically open-minded, and play and humor, among the highest attributes of cultural life, are the key to this openness."

This could apply to my own children who have discovered the world for themselves as they've grown into creative adults and diverse individuals. What all my children share, and what Pagels sees as "the child in us forever exploring," is a sense of awe about nature and a deep appreciation for their natural surroundings. Pagels also spoke for my children and me when he wrote about play and humor as vital to the creative process. For if you don't have a sense of humor and a desire to elevate the people around you, chances are slim that you'll participate in Pagels' "cosmic consciousness of God."

Unlike most of the writers I have discussed, Pagels, the scientist, offered no final answers.

He made it clear he'd rather live with "doubt and uncertainty" than with wrong answers. It's not that he has reached no conclusions, but simply that he was "not absolutely sure of anything." Yet he was not frightened by "being lost in a mysterious universe without any purpose..."

Haunted by the universe, Pagels wrote that it was his "sense of the unfathomable beautiful ocean of existence" that led him into science. He wrote:

> *The scientific story of Genesis begins in 1913 when Vesto Melvin Slipher... discovered that about a dozen galaxies in our vicinity were moving away from us at very high speeds, ranging up to 2 million miles per hour.*

In other words, as scientists rigorously investigated our past origins in terms of physics and astronomy, what they found was the instant of Creation. The theory of evolution is thus seen as compatible with the Old Testament, except for a fundamentalist reading of every word as literally, rather than metaphorically, true.

Evolution is what has allowed our minds to lift us out of the caves and up to our present level of sophistication. We have to hope that evolution will continue to move us forward beyond the use of violence to solve struggles and into an age of renewed enlightenment. Only through such broad thinking will we fully understand our place in the universe. We cannot continue operating under a blanket of misunderstanding about our world and its limited resources.

We have to pull together the world's intelligence to solve the tremendous challenges we face. Technology alone cannot solve them. Religion in itself cannot, nor can government. Our best hopes are to work through the world's universities and to link industry and technology in a union I've called Economicology. Guided by ethical and moral standards, the world's universities offer the best possible mechanism for marrying economics to ecology and saving our planet.

In the Beginning was the Word and the Word was God—and the Big Bang. God, the Creator, the stars, the Earth, mankind—the same elements are in us all. Readers of Heinz Pagels understand this. Students enrolled in Professor Tom Pagliasotti's class "The Prominence of Process in Modern Science and Religion" are starting to grasp this unity concept that could paraphrase the code of the Three Musketeers: all for one and one for all.

Understanding is the reward of faith.
Therefore seek not to understand that thou mayest believe, but believe that thou mayest understand.

St. Augustine

Chapter 20

"Bucky" Fuller and One World Ends All Wars

Earlier in this book, I drew on the wisdom of the man who pioneered in environmental construction, R. Buckminster Fuller. This builder, designer, and original thinker was the person who first drew the world's attention to, and coined the term, "Spaceship Earth." As a self-trained architect, Buckminster Fuller devoted his life to finding structural solutions for the environmental stresses caused by the rapid expansion of the human population. One of his more famous environmental contributions was the geodesic dome created for Ford Motor Company's Detroit factory. With his geodesic dome as prototype, Fuller made an art out of getting the maximum indoor space from the minimum outdoor surface.

"Bucky" Fuller was also the prophetic spokesman for what has to happen if our planet is to survive. It is not new technologies that will save us, Fuller argued, but effectively applying the technologies we already have. The electrical energy network of the world, for instance, is capable of putting all of the world's people on the same economic accounting system. In other words, instead of the variety of world currencies—from drachmas to pounds to marks to yen—that separate nations, Fuller argued that we should trade in one common denomination and in one single, world economy. The euro currency, scheduled to become the common currency of Europe on January 1, 1999, is a positive sign in that direction—one Buckminster Fuller would cheer on.

Fuller thought that integrating the "world's economic interests and value systems" would be the fastest way to eliminate the 170 some sovereign and separate nations of the world. With computers, satellites, and electronic communications systems putting every country next door to every other country now, we are able to link up mankind in a way to end wars forever. We can unite mankind in a way to save the environment. We can unite mankind in a way to end the you-or-me mentality that has driven human history.

Fuller wrote:

> *Most of the tasks that need to be attended to make all humanity sustainingly successful involve only the right application of the already-developed technologies which have been funded and applied to the wrong tasks.*

And the reason the many breath-taking advances in technology have been wrongly used is that the separate nation states have historically been competitive rather than cooperative. With limited resources in the world, so this divisive and wrong thinking goes, we can't all have enough, so let's go to war to decide who gets the most.

Fuller, the philosopher-builder, said:

> *It must be remembered that the overwhelming reason for their* (technologies') *being applied to the wrong tasks is the assumption of those commanding the political and economic power structures that there is a fundamental inadequacy of life support on our planet—that it has to be 'you or me,' nowhere nearly enough for both.*

When the Russians tried to exert what they perceived as their "you or me" ascendancy over Afghanistan, for instance, the Soviet Army brutally invaded the small, undeveloped mountain country. The Russian tanks rolled into Afghanistan as a result of this faulty, not-enough-for-both-of-us thinking. Mistaken in their belief that the world did not have enough energy sources to go around, the Soviet Army mobilized against the smaller country to get their share of Arabian oil. The only way to make sure the USSR got their oil so the "other" side could not get it was to guarantee access to the Indian Ocean. That access route ran right through Afghanistan.

But the world's energy resources *are* adequate, Fuller asserted. What must be done to make sure all nations grasp this major truth is nothing less than "the education of the world," he wrote. The word needs to go out that what we once thought was "inadequate life support for all humanity" can actually be, if used properly "bounteously adequate." We need not wait around for new inventions, said the creative genius, an inventor himself. We need only learn how to apply the technological advances already in our hands to the appropriate tasks.

Critical Path was the culmination of Bucky Fuller's crusade to make our Spaceship Earth a war-free planet. Since he wrote the book in 1981, Communism has finally collapsed making the earth safer from nuclear war than it was when **Critical Path** was published. But we cannot risk letting the ongoing diminishment of super-power animosities lull us into thinking our planet is safe.

On the contrary, Buckminster Fuller said he wrote **Critical Path** "because of my driving conviction that all of humanity is in peril of extinction." What is required of us now is hard-core honesty about the future of this world. We must "dare," in R. Buckminster Fuller's word, to tell the truth now and forever if we are to save ourselves and our globe. The time to begin doing so is "right now."

This great thinker of our times inspired me to write a poem in response to his call for the truth and "only the truth and all the truth." I've titled it "ALL."

ALL
I shall write an ode to all!
All those who deny I exist,
I will show them a trick or two
based on my knowledge of you.
You are shy and unassuming,
Afraid to acknowledge your
Feelings, because others would
stir up the pot of ordinary
society, and you would be
lost in the stew.
Blessed are those who are
not afraid of all, and plan
out their lives in the truth.
For they will be happy in
their own right, and I will
be happy with you.

Like the architect R. Buckminster Fuller, Heinz R. Pagels—the physicist discussed in the previous chapter—understood how swiftly we could destroy ourselves with the technology at our disposal. Again like Bucky Fuller, Pagels wrote as a prophet who could see disaster coming, but who could also see a way to prevent it. Both these brilliant thinkers understood that technology itself is neutral. It's how we use it that can save us and our planet or destroy us.

In his 1982 book, **The Cosmic Code: Quantum Physics As The Language of Nature**,

Pagels echoed Buckminster Fuller when he wrote that the "forces science has discovered in the universe can annihilate us." Yet, with an optimism comparable to Fuller's, Pagels at the same time argued that those same scientific forces also have the potential to make life better and more fulfilling for all the world's peoples.

In his book on quantum physics, Pagels wrote:

> *The challenge to our civilization which has come from our knowledge of cosmic energies that fill the stars, the movement of light and electrons through matter, the intricate molecules' order which is the biological basis of life must be met by the creation of a moral and political order which will accommodate these forces or we shall be destroyed.*

In other words, the crisis is not about man's unprecedented scientific power; the crisis is what man does with it. We are now at a cosmic crossroads. As the physicist Pagels put it, we have arrived at the point in human history where either "those sentences in the cosmic code could bring our existence to an end or, alternatively, be the birth of humanity into the universe." The mechanical tools for doing good or doing evil are the same. And they are in our hands.

In his book, Pagels did not underestimate the task of deciding how to use these powerful tools. He recognized that the "moral and political order" needed will "try our deepest resources of reason and compassion." As individual humans, Pagels said, we are fulfilled because of our feelings and our faith. But as a species, our ability to survive at all will depend on our wise use of reason and knowledge. Pagels' advice harked back to his fellow physicist Albert Einstein.

One of the great scientific minds of all time, Albert Einstein grasped the significance of what he'd done when he discovered the principles of nuclear energy. Einstein recognized that no longer were the scientific advances the most important factors for mankind. With the dawn of a nuclear age, Einstein knew it would be the "moral questions" that mattered most. If humanity is to go on, the man who discovered relativity urged upon us the necessity for creating a moral order.

Buckminster Fuller, Heinz Pagels, and Albert Einstein all understood that our ongoing leaps forward in science would test man's deepest abilities both to reason and to care for each other. Fuller calling for the moral application of technology, Einstein advocated the pursuit of ethics over mathematics, and Pagels urged upon us a "moral and political order." Clearly the three intellectuals stressed different ethical principles, but always toward the same common goal. In their own individual ways, all three scientists understood it would not be our material advances that would stop us from destroying our planet. It would be our moral ones.

A man is ethical only when life, as such, is sacred to him,
that of plants and animals as well as that of his fellowman,
and when he devotes himself helpfully
to all life that is in need of help.

Albert Schweitzer

The salvation of mankind lies only in making everything the concern of all.

Alexander Solzhenitsyn

Chapter 21

Eric Chaisson: Life Era Requires Ethical Evolution

As I conclude this gathering of great minds, I have, in a sense, saved the best for last. Not that my final thinker Eric Chaisson—a foremost astronomer, microbiologist, astrophysicist, and downright good citizen—is more gifted than the others, but that he comes closest to my own philosophy. My theory of Economicology is entirely compatible with what Chaisson has written. My belief that the world's economy and the world's ecology can BOTH thrive through thoughtful planning is well supported by Eric Chaisson.

Eric Chaisson's writings epitomize the clarity of thinking that often comes from a mind balanced in knowledge about both the knowns of science and the unknowns of philosophy. In the prologue to his 1987 book **The Life Era**, Chaisson asserted that we must have an integrated world culture—including a unified political-economic ideology—if we are to have a future. His is not one more hackneyed proposal for a world government, but rather a new way of thinking in big terms that embrace galactical change.

Saying that the "...time is right for a grand synthesis of science—a merger of the biological and physical disciplines," Chaisson recognized the glorious significance of such a blending. He saw the limitless possibilities that would open up when humanity could at last "begin to appreciate how ALL things—from atoms to roses, from galaxies to people—are interrelated."

The epiphany in this recognition that man is essentially one with the universe could change the way we see other peoples and other nations. The result of this new perspective, according to Chaisson, would be that we no longer dissipate our energy on competing and differing national moralities. Instead of fighting over conflicting values, we would have to develop a planet-wide standard of ethics that applies to all people forever.

If we were to act wisely in a fashion beyond mere intelligence in this new discovery of our universal oneness, we would be launching what Chaisson called an era of "ethical evolution." His ethical evolution is the next, and necessary, great leap forward for civilization and for cosmic survival itself. But such a gargantuan jump into universal ethics requires technologically talented life forms, and there's only one. Us. We, the human race, must be the new agents of change in the ethical evolution.

Eric Chaisson clarified the definition of what he termed "cosmic evolution" as only a fancy word for "change." According to Charisson, "Cosmic evolution is the study of the many varied changes in the assembly and composition of energy, matter, and life in the Universe." In other words, Chaisson's "cosmic evolution" is an interpretation of how it all began in the first place, and how it has changed over the millennia of time.

In the beginning was the Energy Era, according to Chaisson, followed by Matter Era. Now begins the Life Era where life plays the organizing role originally held by Energy and then by Matter. What Darwin did for plants and animals with his biological evolution, cosmic evolution now does for ALL things. Darwin freed us from seeing man as different from other life forms and as the center of the planet. Man is like other life forms, Darwin taught us, because he evolved from them; and man is not, Darwin proved, the center of the universe.

Now Chaisson's cosmic evolution similarly reveals to thinking humans that the matter in our bodies and all the matter on earth is no different than the matter in the stars and in the galaxies beyond us. As the physicist Heinz Pagels had similarly explained, we are one with the universe.

But if we are to survive, cosmic evolution among technological civilizations won't suffice. Technical power alone won't save us. The cosmic evolution of sophisticated nations will have to embrace global ethics, or the massive power we have in our grasp will blow up in our collective faces. Chaisson argued that "ethical evolution" will have to be the inevitable next great leap forward in the "overall scheme of cosmic evolution itself." This ethical evolution will happen because it will function as a new kind of natural selection at work. Only those life forms that welcome planetary citizenship will realize the Life Era. Those who think technology alone is adequate will perish.

Chaisson summarized why ethical evolution was crucial to humanity:

To maintain civilization at a reasonably acceptable level of humane peace and order, we need to work at it, to put energy into the system to establish and abide by a set of societal norms that help avert social chaos, anarchy, and barbarism. Such might previously have been called social or cultural evolution, but I prefer to employ the term 'ethical evolution,' for we must now behave more than just socially; we must act ethically and precisely in whatever ways are needed to ensure the longevity of intelligent life on Earth.

In **The Life Era**, published in 1987, Chaisson pointed out that we have accumulated more data in the past few decades than we have through all recorded history put together. We are, in other words, on information overload. At the same time, however, we have also begun to transfer some of our most profound issues of religion and philosophy into the realm of science. In that sense we are on scientific overload at the expense of spirituality. To restore balance, Chaisson called on us to create a "cosmic heritage" incorporating what we've learned from the past to be used as an "intellectual road map" for the present. Such a framework would then become a "virtual blueprint for survival" to future generations.

But to draw on this cosmic heritage for mankind's survival blueprint will require our leaders—many of them with legal or business backgrounds—to become scientists to a degree. Eric Chaisson argued that the great minds in arenas other than science—our social, political, and religious leaders—will have to understand the physics of our cosmos if they are to guide us in dealing with the big picture. Chaisson wrote that this whole-view way of seeing life would help these world figures realize how we fit into the cosmic scheme of things, how fragile yet beautiful our spaceship Earth really is. In doing so, we might just get our earthly act together for the betterment of all humankind.

For example, Chaisson noted, our leaders must learn how the savings account of Earth's atmospheric thermal energy could be depleted in a matter of months. Even faster, the latent heat in our oceans could disappear in only weeks. With even more alacrity could come the decline of any mechanical energy—such as the atmospheric circulation of weather—which could happen in a few days.

In short, Earth's ultimate source of energy will not be located on Earth, nor can we depend on Earth for our future water needs. Chaisson recognized that such drastic information needed to be grasped scientifically by the heads of every church and nation so they would intellectually understand the gravity of the situation. Their full comprehension of the scientific evidence would stir them to act in time.

In harsh terms of reality, Chaisson wrote that the mature "Life Era" he saw as pivotal to our survival might never happen. Yet, with blazing hope that it could, he called the late 20th Century a revolutionary opportunity "in the history of the Universe." Chaisson saw that we have learned enough to finally begin "to unlock secrets of the Universe, indeed to decipher who we really are and whence we came." This intellectual power, this ability to reflect upon the material forces of life, gives us an unprecedented cosmic control over matter. We now understand, for instance, that our Earth is subject to internal chemical and thermal blasts as well as external assaults from countless asteroids and comets.

Eric Chaisson spoke for me as well when he wrote that what we do in the next few decades will determine whether or not life on this planet has a future at all. We are threatened, he wrote, by the "foremost issues of overpopulation and nuclear warfare to genetic degeneration and environmental pollution." These are problems on a risk scale never faced by our ancestors. And these problems are not limited to one nation over another.

As Chaisson put it in no uncertain terms:

> *Ours are global problems. For the first time in history civilization faces not just village, national, or even regionally international problems, but large-scale debilitative issues that, should they go unchecked, threaten not merely to lessen the quality of human life but, without exaggeration, to extinguish it over much of our planet.*

And none of these historical threats to existence is going away. No people in human history have ever had to deal with such end-time issues before. We must face the seriousness of what today's choices mean for any future at all. Maybe we'll ask the wrong questions as we search our way to solutions. But, as Chaisson said, "Not to ask them at all is to constrain the life of understanding."

Chaisson saw our solutions coming from an accelerated form of evolution that will turn our divided world into one "global culture." We must, he asserted, name and embrace ethical laws that will govern the whole planet. These universal moral laws will direct human attitudes and behaviors toward what is best not just for us and our country, but "for all humankind." In short, the words "future" and "ethical" have to become synonymous. Like the Six Es of Ecology, Economy, Environment, Ethics, Empathy, and Education, we must integrate the best we have in one unified and universal system of values.

And the core of these global ethics will not be rules rigid and immutable, but rather laws that allow for "change and adaptability" as times change. We have to begin by rethinking ourselves as "first and foremost citizens of a planet." Our existence as a member of one particular nation is only secondary. "It is essential that we broaden our outlook in all respects," Chaisson summarized.

Chaisson went as far as to advocate restrictions on individual liberty if that is what it will take to launch his new "ethical evolution." He reached this freedom-restrictive conclusion reluctantly as a result of too many years observing the selfish self-interest of individuals fighting what is best for the entire human race. He wrote:

> *...I now embrace the cause of humanity as a whole, including, if necessary, the greater regulation of society and the diminished liberty of individuals that are apparently required to ensure survival of a technological civilization. To state it in terse though telling terms, people should always be free to destroy themselves but should not be free to destroy the species.*

The only way to resolve this struggle between what's right for me versus what's right for the human race is the intellectual position of the cosmic evolutionist. We can no longer put "me" separate and first, but rather we must begin thinking in terms of unity and globalism.

Referring to Hegel's philosophy of history as a synthesis of polar forces, Chaisson speculated that what might be needed today is an almost Hegelian "merger" to a higher order. For Chaisson, Hegel's thesis and antithesis stand for the political extremes of individuality in the world's democracies versus state socialism typified in Communism. Chaisson called this ultimate blend of individual liberty and state control—Hegel's synthesis—"evolutionary humanism." Anticipating the outcry from the Western nations over any curtailment of their rights and freedoms, Chaisson argued that "the individual must be willing to sacrifice—and that may well include curbing free will to some extent."

Chaisson did not believe individuals were ready to make this sacrifice of individual rights. Consequently, he thought a "system of laws and penalties" would have to be enacted either by governments or the world's religions. He wrote:

> *To maintain civilization at a reasonably acceptable level of humane peace and order, we need to work at it, to put energy into the system, to establish and abide by a set of societal norms that help avert social chaos, anarchy, and barbarism.*

Traditionally called "cultural evolution," Chaisson referred to these necessary "laws and penalties" as "ethical evolution."

In spite of his lack of faith that individuals would freely choose to sacrifice, Chaisson was not pessimistic about the ability of mankind itself to choose his ethical evolution. The global society Chaisson advocated was to him a normal part of evolution. **The Life Era** simply marked the beginning of man's significant influence over his own destiny. "But we must be willing to accept change, to welcome it," he wrote. He saw change to be simply a law of nature, and perhaps change itself, he speculated, was actually "the only real ethic."

Yet even if change is indeed the single ethic, Chaisson did not underestimate the disasters that can occur when change comes too quickly. As examples of radical changes happening too fast, Chaisson cited both Afghanistan's rush toward democracy and Grenada's "flirtation with socialism." Such drastic revolutions to Chaisson were *not* substitutes for evolution. But he wondered if we can "afford to wait for the evolutionary process" to happen? "Can we run the risk that even a single global issue—say, overpopulation or nuclear warfare—could remain unsolved long enough to overwhelm us?"

Chaisson went on to quote the British philosopher Bertrand Russell who seemed to have a crystal ball when he had addressed the same theme earlier this century. Russell had written:

> *We appeal as human beings, to human beings; remember your humanity and forget the rest. If you can do so, the way lies open to a new Paradise; if you cannot, there lies before you the risk of universal death.*

Bertrand Russell's appeal foreshadowed Eric Chaisson's "ethical evolution" in **The Life Era**.

Only education, Chaisson summarized, can help us convert our egocentric mindsets to the acceptance of a different, broader perspective for surviving on our "ever-shrinking planet." Education might not be able to make us enthusiastic about the necessary adjustments and sacrifices we must make as individuals; but at least it can teach us to tolerate them. And why should the individual—mostly in the Western world—have to make what would seem to be the far greater sacrifice? The answer is simple. "...the most basic interest of the human genes to enhance the survival of our species" requires it.

Chaisson labeled mankind's genetic call to survival "enlightened self-interest." By devoting ourselves to the welfare of all people, we end up promoting our own interests. And the greatest self-interest of all is on behalf of saving the human gene. The instinct for survival—the most powerful force in biological evolution—will "certainly play a principal role in ethical evolution as well."

In the course of this ethical evolution, one of the major adjustments we'll have to make is reworking what we admire in other people. Where now the narrowly focused, relentless man of ambition is our role model for success, we must begin to see people of broader vision as our exemplars. We must replace our current hero who excels at niche thinking with the new Renaissance man who pursues a broad spectrum of learning. The father of the scientific method, Francis Bacon summarized the vast scope of his own studies when he wrote that he had "taken all knowledge to be my province."

Unfortunately, Francis Bacon's wide frame of reference is not what is happening in the scientific community anymore. Indeed, today's natural scientists seem not to realize they have a professional obligation to make their knowledge available to the general public. We can no longer afford to let our academic scientists isolate themselves in ivory towers oblivious to humanity's greater needs. Rather they must descend into the mainstream and make scientists of us all if the human gene is to go on. It is precisely this widespread dissemination of scientific information that Chaisson saw as pivotal to his "ethical evolution."

Chaisson—an astronomer, microbiologist, and astrophysicist himself—posed an ominous question to his colleagues in the science community for not educating the public at large. He asked pointedly, "Will the scientific academy adapt to the changing environment and begin articulating knowledge capably, or will it effectively face extinction as an institution useless to humankind?"

I have to believe our top scientists and thinkers will, indeed, come forth to educate mankind about what must be done in our changing environment. I close this chapter by quoting one of our nation's first, and certainly one of our most articulate environmentalists. My own optimism is summarized in his words.

I know of no more encouraging fact
than the unquestionable ability of man
to elevate his life by a conscious endeavor.

Henry David Thoreau

Thou shalt not commit abuse
against the Earth and its life support system,
but rather honor it
with respect for sustaining life,
as we know it.

P.M.W.

Epilogue

Choosing the word "ominously" to describe Eric Chaisson's question to his fellow scientists in the previous chapter was not accidental. What you have just read—this collection of great thinkers—is nothing less than the most frightening warning in all human history. If we continue to treat our planet as if its supply of sustenance were infinite, we guarantee our world and all life on it will come to an end. Not until we take definitive action from the advice of the writers gathered in this book do we take "ominous" out of our future and replace it with "ongoing."

I've written this book to bring together these great writers—these brave prophets who have tried to educate us about the consequences of our actions. Their warnings need to be shouted from the house tops. They need to be heard by our religious and government leaders and everyone else who has not yet grasped the enormity of our environmental problems.

Instead of joining hands to reach a common ideal of global survival, we have been too preoccupied with individual and national power struggles. It will take the benevolent understanding of all world leaders to preserve our spinning Earth. It will take a higher level of intelligence. It will take the compassion of all people.

Not until every religion and all national powers decide to end their territorial struggles can our planet hope to survive. Not until greed, avarice, envy, and ignorance have been replaced by generosity, compassion, and education will all the peoples of the earth survive—and even thrive.

As I was recently driving out to my little farm house to put the finishing touches on this collected wisdom of the past and present, I wondered if it was all worth it? Reflecting on what I've tried to do here, my mind flashed back to my early days at a small Catholic grade school. I still remember my kind kindergarten teacher at St. Stephens, Sister Mary Leonard. And I remember with fondness Sister Vincent de Paul, my marvelous seventh-grade teacher.

Perhaps I never fully realized the importance those devoted teachers played in my life until I returned from World War II in a snowstorm. I was still carrying the holy medal they had given me to keep me safe when I left for the service.

Yes, writing this book *has* been worth all all the effort just as everything those good sisters imparted to me was worth all that they gave. What they taught me about loving God and being a good steward to everything He created has much to do with why I wrote this book.

In the half century since I came home from World War II to meet my ten-month old daughter Mary for the first time, our country has "progressed" by putting millions more air-polluting vehicles on the roads. But all we've really managed to do by parking two gas-guzzling cars in every garage is to bottle up traffic and pollute the air. Instead of building an efficient mass-transportation system to preserve the environment, we've let the auto war lords convince us that everyone who can drive needs his own car.

But if we truly want our environment to thrive and our economy to prosper, we must convince our leaders to act in everyone's best interest by building the finest railroad system in the world. We desperately need good railroads to augment what used to be the finest highway system in the world. If hindsight is 20-20 vision, then it is now clear that the Big Three Auto companies should be transportation companies. Instead of producing a new car every few minutes, they should work with the federal and state governments on building a reliable mass-transportation system for people within our big cities and to and from our major population areas.

It is truly inexcusable that in the world's richest, most powerful nation there is still no safe, dependable, inexpensive mass-transportation connecting our major cities—either from coast to coast or from south to north. But it is not too late. The right-of-ways already in place could become the tracks over which efficient, non-polluting, and fast trains move. It is just as inexcusable that the United States still has electrical power coming from deteriorating nuclear power plants with no suitable safe storage of the waste materials.

Simple, everyday changes of habit—using one paper towel instead of two—help sustain our natural resources. Americans are only 6% of the world's people, but we use 36% of the world's natural resources. That is inexcusable.

What is inexcusable above all else is our world's uncontrolled population growth. The carrying capacity of this planet has already been reached in many areas of the globe, but the birth rates still keep climbing! Too many people for too few resources will bring catastrophic destruction to the eco-system which ultimately must serve a sustainable economy.

My philosophy as an "Economicologist" has been trying to make people see there are limits to growth, starting with how many humans our planet can support. With over five billion people on earth by early 1993, we are already out of control in terms of population. Does this mean we should throw our hands up and quit? Not at all. For people of conscience and spirituality can—and will—understand that these over-population troubles are a result of man's evolutionary climb. Now man must take the next evolutionary step to cure the crowding troubles he has created.

For everything threatening the life-support system of Earth is either a direct or indirect result of the world's excessive birth rate. Whether it is Earth's temperature, or the topsoil lost to the sea, or the acres lost to deserts, or the extinction of living species, all the forces destroying our globe emanate from too many people drawing from one fixed well or resources.

"What man has made, man can change," was the motto for the Center for Environmental Study I founded 25 years ago. I had the support of many who cared about their community—a true cross section of doctors, teachers, laborers, students, lawyers, city workers, industrialists. They served on task forces researching air, water, liquid, and organic-waste pollution. The good people at our Center made recommendations to improve the environment, and the public was delighted.

My dream then is my dream now, only it is bigger. Today we need not just community members, but we need people from governments and industries who will join forces with the researchers and scientists. My fervent hope is that the world's religions and nation states will set aside their differences and work toward the common goal of survival by becoming both enlightened and caring.

This book aims to address the environmental threats we face, but in a positive, hopeful, and educational manner. The nation's business schools—who were late in recognizing the importance of ecological planning—need to teach the new generation of business leaders the principles of Economicology. Blacker bottom-line ink and a cleaner environment ARE entirely compatible.

Ronald Higgins in **The Seventh Enemy** described what he saw as the seven main threats to mankind's survival. I find all seven of them frighteningly on target. Yet I would add two more. Higgins' list begins with the central problem that leads to all the others: population explosion. His other six are: food shortage; scarcity of natural resources; pollution and degradation of the environment; high- and low-level nuclear waste; uncontrolled technology; moral blindness; and political inertia.

To Higgins' list of seven, I would add two more. First, the human frailties of avarice and greed must be overcome. And, finally, we must end the religious warfare that prevents us from becoming one world under God for the benefit of all mankind.

If we are to survive the fatal truth of Higgins' Seven list and Wege's Two More, several things must occur. World leaders from every nation must be educated about the disastrous consequences to our planet if we continue to over-populate ourselves. Too many people means we will pollute our air and our water while at the same time drowning ourselves in waste!

If civilization is to continue, we must elevate the educational level of the masses so they can understand the threat to all life that comes from having too many people on the planet. Experts in the life sciences must come together at the highest levels to collaborate on the best means for combating over-population.

We must continue to study the glaring evidence that global warming is caused by the density of population in the major cities who produce waste heat and carbon dioxide. We can no longer ignore the statistics on the growing hole in the ozone layer and the increase in the Earth's temperature.

We must preserve sufficient farm land to produce enough food rather than continue to develop precious acreage for excessively big homes and endless strip malls. We have to clean up the nuclear wastes and devote our talents to developing solar energy world wide.

So why do so few people recognize the seriousness of Earth's predicament? It is in the best interests of consumer economics not to tell. And if short-term profits are a company's driving objective, making money at the expense of the ecology is still a plus for that business. It is this economy-above-all mindset that spurred me to write this book.

I am certainly not opposed to profit making. Nor have I ever advocated the American economy must play dead for the sake of the ecology. But I also do not believe we can let the bottom line dictate how we treat our planet. Economicology means the economy and ecology *can* work in synergy, each helping the other flourish.

I urge everyone to go back and read the entire books from which I have quoted. You will see how we are all in this thing together on our precious Spaceship Earth. We will survive or vanish depending on how we respond to the words of these loving scientists and philosophers. Let us see if we care enough to gather the forces of compassion in a wave so strong it will overcome other selfish forces now exploiting God, nature, and mankind.

We as a people must understand we are one family under God—we are one eco-system and one planet in an infinity of space and time. We must bring our minds and hearts to bear on keeping this extremely complicated system alive and well. It is our home, and we can no longer sweep mankind's destructive ways under our environmental rug. What we must begin with is changing our mind sets as to why we are here at all. We must begin to understand life. Air, water, and natural foods were abundant for us when life was simple. But as the population grew, we failed to plan for the long-range demands of providing for more and more people.

We must now learn how to preserve, protect, and sustain our natural resources. We must come together as a planetary family to map our futures based on Economics, Ecology, Environment, Ethics, Empathy, and Education. The Six Es must be bound together in a balancing act for survival. Nothing less than all countries, all religions, and all cultures working together will keep civilization from collapsing.

I call it Economicology.

I call it E to the 6th power.

I call it the Eleventh Commandment!

Isn't it time we had the intelligence, love, and compassion to make it work? The future will run rough-shod over us if we refuse to see that only the wealth of the heart, mind, and spirit will direct the right path of evolution. Evolution is bringing us kicking and screaming into the reality that tells us what we must do as responsible passengers on Spaceship Earth.

I believe this E to the 6th power meets our spiritual and moral needs as well as helping us understand our planet. If we act in this E 6 spirit to make long-range plans rather than reacting out of desperation and fear, Earth WILL survive.

Consider this description of our world from Rene Dubos' book, **A God Within**, and ask yourself if this spinning planet we call home is worth saving:

> *The earth with its vistas of breathtaking beauty, its azure seas, beaches, mighty mountains, and soft blanket of forest and steppe is a veritable wonderland in the universe. It is a gem of rare and magic beauty hung in a trackless space filled with lethal radiations and accompanied in its journey by sister planets which are either viciously hot or dreadfully cold, arid, and lifeless chunks of raw rock. Earth is choice, precious, and sacred beyond all comparison or measure.*

Don't you think it's time for all of us to get into the fight to save our Earth? And we can start right now. You and your community have the people power to begin in your own back yards if you only have the will to do it. Today, not tomorrow, is the time for all good people to come to the aid of our planet's life-support system. I, for one, believe Americans *do* have the will to keep the preservation of Earth moving forward in high gear.

"Caring for Creation" is not an idle statement, but a credo to guide us on a daily basis. For even though all living creatures are affected by pollution, only man has the ability to do something about it.

Children of the human race
Offspring of our Mother Earth,
Not alone in endless space
Has our planet given birth.
Far across the cosmic skies
And from untold planets rise
Endless canticles of praise.

Should some sign of others reach
This, our lonely planet Earth,
Differences of form and speech
Must not hide our common worth.
When at length our minds are free
And the clouds of fear disperse,
Then at least we'll learn to be
Children of the Universe.

—John Andrew Storey

Bibliography and Recommended reading list for

ECONOMICOLOGY by Peter M. Wege

References:

Athanasiou, Tom — *Divided Planet: The Ecology of Rich and Poor*
Little, Brown & Co. — 1996

Barrow, John D. & Frank J. Tipler — *The Anthropic Cosmological Principle*
Oxford University Press — 1986

Berry, Thomas — *The Dream of the Earth*
Sierra Club Books — 1988

Borgstrom, Georg — *The Food and People Dilemma*
Duxbury Press — 1973

Brooks, Jim — *Origins of Life*
A Lion Book: Belleville, MI — 1985

Brown, Lester R., Christopher Flavin & Sandra Postel — *Saving the Planet*
W. W. Norton — 1991

Brown, Lester R. — *The State of the World: A Worldwatch Institute Report*
W. W. Norton — 1991

Carson, Rachel — *Silent Spring*
Houghton Mifflin Co. — 1987 (1962)

Chaisson, Eric — *The Life Era: Cosmic Selection and Conscious Evolution*
Atlantic Monthly Press — 1987

Commoner, Barry — *The Closing Circle*
Bantam Books — 1980

Daly, Herman E. — *Steady-State Economics*
W. H. Freeman — 1977

Daly, Herman E. (ed.) — *Toward a Steady-State Economy*
W. H. Freeman — 1973

de Chardin, Teilhard — *The Phenomenon of Man*
Perennial Library — 1975 (1959)

Dubos, Rene — *A God Within*
Charles Scribner's Sons — 1972

Durrell, Lee — *The State of the Ark: Atlas of Conservation in Action*
Doubleday — 1986

Freedman, Jonathan L. — *Crowding and Behavior*
W. H. Freeman — 1975

Fuller, R. Buckminster — *Critical Path*
St. Martin's Press — 1981

Fuller, R. Buckminster — *Operation Manual for Spaceship Earth*
Clarion/Simon & Schuster — 1969

Gardner, John W. — *On Leadership*
Free Press/Macmillan Co. — 1990

Gardner, John/Task Force on Environmental Health & Related Problems — *A Strategy for a Livable Environment*
Government Printing Office: Washington, D.C. — 1967

Goldsmith, Edward — *The Way: An Ecological World-View*
Shambhala Publications, Inc. — 1993

Gradwohl, Judith & Russell Greenberg — *Saving the Tropical Forest*
Island Press — 1988

Graham, Frank Jr. — *Since Silent Spring*
Houghton Mifflin Co. — 1970

Gribbin, John — *The Hole in the Sky*
Bantam Books — 1988

Halacy, D. S. — *The Coming Age of Solar Energy*
Avon Books — 1975 Revised edition

Hansen, Warren G. — *St. Francis of Assisi: Patron Saint of the Environment*
Franciscan Herald Press — 1971

Hawking, Stephen W. — *Brief History of Time*
Bantom Books — 1988

Hecht, Susan & Alexander Cockburn — *The Fate of the Forest: Developers, Destroyers and Defenders of the Amazon*
Harper Perennial — 1990

Heilbroner, Robert — *An Inquiry into the Human Prospect*
W. W. Norton — 1991 Revised edition

Henderson, Hazel — *Creating Alternative Futures: The End of Economics*
Berkley — 1978

Heppenheimer, T. A. — *Toward Distant Suns*
Stackpole Books — 1979

Higgins, Ronald — *The Seventh Enemy*
McGraw-Hill Publishing Co. — 1978

Hoyle, Fred — *The Ten Faces of the Universe*
W. H. Freeman — 1977

Hynes, H. Patricia — *Earth Right: Every Citizen's Guide*
Prima Publishing — 1990

Jackson, Dixie S. — *Who Needs Nature*
John Wiley & Sons, Inc. — 1973

Jastrow, Robert — *God and the Astronomers*
W. W. Norton — 1978

King, David C. — *International Education for Spaceship Earth*
Foreign Policy Research Institute — 1971

Krishnamurti, J. — *The Future is Now*
Harper & Row Publishers, Inc. — 1989

Lenssen, Nicholas — *Worldwatch Paper #111: Empowering Development, The New Energy Equation*
Worldwatch Institute — November, 1992

Leon, George deLucenay — *Energy Forever: Power for Today and Tomorrow*
Arco Publishing — 1982

Levenson, Thomas — *Ice Time: Climate, Science and Life on Earth*
Harper & Row Publishers, Inc. — 1989

McKibben, Bill — *The End of Nature*
Random House, Inc. — 1989

Meadows, Donella H., Dennis L. Meadows, Jorgen Randers & William W. Behrens III — *The Limits to Growth*
Signet/New American Library — 1972

Meeker-Lowry, Susan — *Economics as if the Earth Really Mattered*
New Society Publishers — 1988

Morris, Desmond — *The Human Zoo*
McGraw-Hill Publishing Co. — 1969

Myers, Norman (ed.) — *GAIA: An Atlas of Planet Management*
Anchor/Doubleday — 1984

Null, Gary — *Man and His Whole Earth*
Stackpole Books — 1976

Pagels, Heinz R. Simon & Schuster	*The Cosmic Code: Quantum Physics as the Language of Nature* 1982
Pagels, Heinz R. Simon & Schuster	*Perfect Symmetry: Search for the Beginning of Time* 1985
Postel, Sandra W. W. Norton	*Last Oasis: Facing the Water Scarcity* 1992
Presidential Science Advisory Committee Government Printing Office: Washington, D.C.	*Restoring the Quality of Our Environment* 1965
Reed, Charles B. Ann Arbor Science Publishers	*Fuels, Minerals and Human Survival* 1975
Regenstein, Lewis Macmillan Co.	*The Politics of Extinction* 1975
Revkin, Andrew Houghton Mifflin Co.	*The Burning Season* 1990
Robertson, James River Basin: St. Paul	*The Sane Alternative* 1978
Schneider, Stephen H. Sierra Club Books	*Global Warming* 1989
Schneider, Stephen H. with Lynne E. Mesirow Plenum Publishing	*The Genesis Strategy; Climate and Global Survival* 1976
Schumacher, E.F. Abacus/Sphere: London	*Small is Beautiful; A Study of Economics as if People Mattered* 1974
Sigma Xi Forum Proceedings	*Global Change and the Human Prospect* 1992

Steger, Will & John Bowermaster Alfred A. Knopf, Inc.	*Saving the Earth* 1990
Still, Henry Tower Natural Heritage	*The Dirty Animal* 1977
Stulman, Julius (ed.) World Institute Council	*Fields Within Fields #11* Spring, 1974
Stulman, Julius (ed.) World Institute Council	*Fields Within Fields #12* Summer, 1974
Toynbee, Arnold Oxford University Press	*A Study of History* 1972 Revised edition
Trefil, J. Charles Scribner's Sons	*Reading the Mind of God: In Search of the Principle of Universality* 1989
Vacca, Roberto Doubleday	*The Coming Dark Age* 1973
Vernadsky, Vladimir Synergetic Press	*The Biosphere* 1986 (1929)
Verney, Peter Mills & Boon Ltd.	*Homo Tyrannicus: History of Man's War Against Animals* 1979
Weiner, Jonathan Bantam Books	*Planet Earth* 1986
Weiner, Jonathan Bantam Books	*The Next 100 Years: Shaping the Fate of Our Living Earth* 1990
Wells, H. G. Alliance Book Corp./ Longmans, Green & Co.	*The Fate of Man* 1939
Wilson, E. O. (ed.) National Academy Press	*Biodiversity* 1988

Young, Louise B.	*The Unfinished Universe*
Simon & Schuster	1986
	Issues in Science and Technology
National Academy of Science	Summer, 1990
	Issues in Science and Technology
National Academy of Science	Winter, 1991